snags and s

A PRACTICAL GUIDE TO EVERYDAY

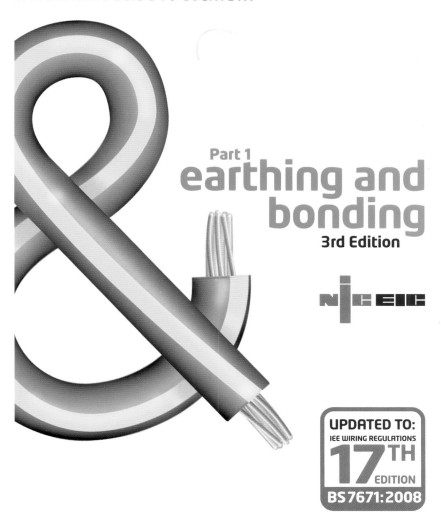

Part 1
earthing and bonding
3rd Edition

NICEIC

UPDATED TO:
IEE WIRING REGULATIONS
17TH EDITION
BS 7671:2008

Practical advice on the application of BS 7671
(17th edition of the IEE Wiring Regulations) provided by NICEIC.

 Published by NICEIC. © Electrical Safety Council (JAN 2008) (3rd Ed.)

NICEIC

'NICEIC' is a trading name of NICEIC Group Limited, a wholly owned subsidiary of the Electrical Safety Council. Under licence from the Electrical Safety Council, NICEIC acts as the electrical contracting industry's independent voluntary regulatory body for electrical installation safety matters throughout the UK, and maintains and publishes registers of electrical contractors that it has assessed against particular scheme requirements (including the technical standard of electrical work).

The registers include the national Roll of Approved Contractors (established in 1956), and the register of NICEIC Domestic Installers that, since January 2005, have been authorised to self-certify their domestic electrical installation work as compliant with the Building Regulations for England and Wales.

The NICEIC Approved Contractor scheme is accredited by the United Kingdom Accreditation Service (UKAS) to *EN 45011 – General requirements for bodies operating product certification systems.*

The Electrical Safety Council

The Electrical Safety Council (formerly the National Inspection Council for Electrical Installation Contracting) is a charitable non-profit making organization set up in 1956 to protect users of electricity against the hazards of unsafe and unsound electrical installations.

The Electrical Safety Council is supported by all sectors of the electrical industry, approvals and research bodies, consumer interest organizations, the electricity distribution industry, professional institutes and institutions, regulatory bodies, trade and industry associations and federations, trade unions and local and central government.

Published by:
NICEIC Group Limited
Warwick House, Houghton Hall Park, Houghton Regis, Dunstable, Bedfordshire LU5 5ZX
Tel: 0870 013 0382   Fax: 01582 556024
Email: enquiries@niceic.com Website: www.niceicgroup.com

ISBN 10	0-9531058-7-3
ISBN 13	978-0-9531058-7-8
EAN	9780953105878

Snags and Solutions

'Snags and Solutions', NICEIC's most requested problem-solving book, is back with a new volume featuring 53 commonly-encountered earthing and bonding dilemmas.

The previous, March 2006, edition of Snags and Solutions is now revised to incorporate the requirement of *BS 7671: 2008 (17th Edition of the IEE Wiring Regulations)*.

This handy pocket-sized book explains many of the common misconceptions about earthing and bonding. Snag 1 explains the difference between earthing and bonding, while snag 2 elaborates on the standard types of earthing arrangements for electrical systems. Snags 3-53 throw light on many earthing and bonding predicaments.

Every snag and corresponding solution is clearly illustrated, and concludes with reference to the relevant requirements of *BS 7671*.

This new edition is fully updated to reflect the requirements of *BS 7671: 2008* (IEE Wiring Regulations 17th edition).

Other available Electrical Safety Council and NICEIC publications include:

The NICEIC Inspection, Testing and Certification book

The fifth edition of the NICEIC Inspection, Testing and Certification book gives valuable help on performing inspection and testing, and with completing the certificates and reports required by *BS 7671: Requirements for Electrical Installations*, the national safety standard. The book covers the general requirements relating to the inspection and testing, and the completion of certificates for electrical installations forming part of TN-C-S, TN-S and TT systems. It is intended to instruct the trained and experienced person both to undertake the inspection and testing of electrical installations and to fill in the appropriate certificates and report forms.

The Electrical Safety Council Technical Manual

The Electrical Safety Council Technical Manual gives detailed advice and guidance on the application of the requirements of *BS 7671*. As at September 2007, the Manual consists of more than 350 topics. The Manual is updated twice a year both with new and revised topics.

The Technical Manual is fast becoming the essential reference document on electrical installation safety matters, and the definitive guide to complying with the requirements of *BS 7671* and related standards, for the electrical contracting industry and other qualified practitioners.

It comprises discrete articles, or 'Topics', each of which concentrates on an electrical installation issue of interest to electrical installation contractors, electrical engineers, electrical installation designers, college lecturers, electrical equipment manufacturers and the members of those committees responsible for the production of national and industry standards for electrical installations, equipment and products. The relevant requirements of *BS 7671* (IEE Wiring Regulations), British Standards and other Industry Codes of Practice are identified and amplified, and their implications explained. Many topics also incorporate data and other useful information on the subjects they cover.

The Technical Manual will build up to cover some 800 topics, clearly illustrated and in full colour. It will be regularly updated to incorporate the latest developments.

The intended users of the Technical Manual are persons trained to at least National Vocational Qualification (NVQ) Level 2 in electrical installation work, and having a good understanding of the requirements of *BS 7671* and related standards.

Copyright acknowledgments

The Electrical Safety Council and NICEIC Group Limited extend their thanks to the organizations that have given permission for extracts from their publications to be reproduced in this book, particularly the Institution of Engineering Technology and the British Standards Institution.

Also acknowledged is the support of the electrical manufacturers who have provided graphic material relating to their products or services for reproduction in the book. Whilst acknowledging such support, however, the Electrical Safety Council and NICEIC Group Limited wish to make it clear that the inclusion of such material in this publication does not signify that a product or service has in any way been endorsed or is being promoted by them.

Foreword

Bathrooms

The 2001 amendment to *BS 7671* required provision of local supplementary equipotential bonding connecting together the terminal of the protective conductor of each circuit supplying Class I and Class II equipment in zones 1, 2 or 3, and extraneous-conductive-parts in these zones.

This requirement has changed in *BS 7671: 2008*. In general, where all final circuits of the location containing a bath or shower:

- comply with the requirements for automatic disconnection according to Regulation 411.3.2, and

- have additional protection by means of an RCD having the characteristics of Regulation 415.1.1, and

- where all extraneous-conductive-parts are effectively connected to the protective equipotential bonding according to Regulation 411.3.1.2

then no supplementary bonding is required. (Regulation 701.415.2 refers)

To comply with each of the bullet points listed above:

i) Regulation 411.3.2 requires that for final circuits having a rating not exceeding 32 A the maximum disconnection time under fault conditions for a 230 V nominal supply is:

- 0.4 s for TN systems, and

- 0.2 s for TT systems.

For final circuits exceeding 32 A and for distribution circuits a maximum disconnection time of:

- 5 s for TN systems, and

- 1 s for TT systems

is permitted.

ii) An RCD having the characteristics required by Regulation 415.1.1 has a rated residual operating current ($I_{\Delta n}$) not exceeding 30 mA and an operating time not exceeding 40 ms at a residual current of $5I_{\Delta n}$).

iii) Regulation 411.3.1.2 requires that main protective bonding conductors complying with Chapter 54 shall connect to the main earthing terminal extraneous-conductive-parts including:

- water installation pipes

- gas installation pipes

- other installation pipework and ducting

- central heating and air conditioning systems

- exposed metallic structural parts of the building

- connection of a lightning protection system made in accordance with the requirements of *BS EN 62305*.

Snag 51 deals with new installations, whether a rewire or a new build.

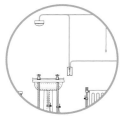

Snag 52 deals with the addition of a new circuit to an existing installation

Snag 53 deals with the alteration of an existing circuit to an existing installation.

What are Earthing and Bonding and why are they so important?

Earthing

Earthing is the connection of the 'exposed-conductive-parts' of an installation to the main earthing terminal of that installation.

An exposed-conductive-part is the conductive part of equipment which can be touched and which is not normally live, but which can become live when basic insulation fails. The purpose of earthing is to direct a fault current to earth and cause the faulty circuit to disconnect, preventing a current from travelling directly through a person and preventing a risk of fire from the faulty circuit.

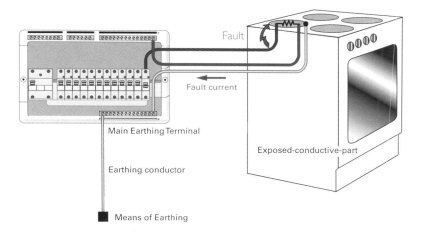

Fault

Fault current

Main Earthing Terminal

Earthing conductor

Means of Earthing

Exposed-conductive-part

The example shows how earthing works. If a fault occurs, the fault current flows through the circuit found by the earth fault loop. The protective device disconnects the fault and prevents the metal case of the cooker from being an electric shock risk or the faulty circuit being a fire risk.

Main Equipotential Bonding

Bonding, or protective bonding, is an electrical connection maintaining various exposed-conductive-parts and extraneous-conductive-parts at substantially the same potential.

The purpose of bonding is to reduce any risk of electric shock by connecting together metallic parts with protective bonding conductors.

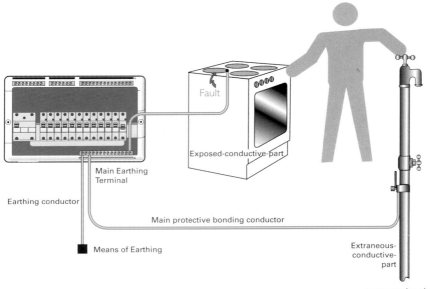

In the diagram, the person is at risk of electric shock due to a potential difference between the faulty cooker and the metal water tap and pipe.

The main protective bonding conductor reduces the risk of electric shock by connecting together the faulty cooker (an exposed-conductive-part) and the water pipe and tap (an extraneous-conductive-part).

Supplementary Equipotential Bonding

Supplementary equipotential bonding (supplementary bonding for short) involves connecting together the conductive parts of electrical and non-electrical items such as those shown in the figure to prevent the occurrence of a dangerous voltage between them under earth fault conditions.

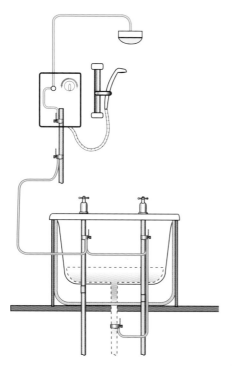

Note that the connections shown do not necessarily represent actual cable routes.

In this book, reference is frequently made to exposed-conductive-parts and extraneous-conductive-parts. It is worthwhile to give the definitions and some examples of these parts:

Exposed-conductive-part

Conductive part of equipment which can be touched and which is not normally live, but which can become live when basic insulation fails.

Such parts generally include central heating boilers, metal light fittings, metalclad socket-outlets and brass switches, built-in washing machines and dishwashers, steel conduit and trunking systems, and electric pumps.

Extraneous-conductive-part

A conductive part liable to introduce a potential, generally earth potential, and not forming part of the electrical installation.

Such parts generally include metallic gas installation pipes, water installation pipes, oil pipes, metallic waste pipes, metallic central heating pipes and radiators, accessible metallic structural parts of a building, metallic steelwork, ventilation ducting and air conditioning systems, metallic baths and shower basins.

Index

Main Earthing Terminal

...ductor

▶ Snag 8 **Earthing clamps not to be used on cables**

Earthing clamps must not be used on paper insulated/lead sheathed cables or steel wire armoured cables

▶ Snag 9 **Corrosion at earthing and bonding connections**

Electrolytic action will result in corrosion at earthing and bonding connections

▶ Snag 10 **Z_S values for TT systems**

For a suitably designed installation forming part of a TT system, an earth electrode resistance not exceeding 200 Ω can, in many cases, be considered to be satisfactory

▶ Snag 11 **Main equipotential bonding not provided**

Older installations may be found not to include main equipotential bonding or to have main protective bonding conductors with cross-sectional area (csa) less than that required by *BS 7671*

▶ Snag 12 ***BS 951* Earthing and bonding clamps**

Instances are observed of *BS 951* clamps not being used as intended

▶ Snag 13 **Lightning protection systems**

Lightning protection systems should be connected to the Main Earthing Terminal (MET)

▶ Snag 14 **Gas pipework**

A main protective bonding conductor must be connected to the gas installation pipe

---

Earthing and Bonding   snags and solutions part 1

▶ **Snag 22** **Unused cores of multicore cables**

It is advisable to properly terminate unused cores of a multicore cable

▶ **Snag 23** **Damaged circuit protective conductors**

Precautions must be taken so that cables are not damaged during installation

▶ **Snag 24** **Unearthed sections of conduit**

A single-phase lighting installation consisting of fibreglass and polycarbonate IP65 impact resistant, vandal resistant luminaires is connected by lengths of metal conduit

▶ **Snag 25** **Armour must be earthed**

The armour of a steel wire armoured (swa) cable should always be earthed where fault protection is provided by the measure Automatic Disconnection of Supply

▶ **Snag 26** **Protective conductor run to an accessory but not terminated**

Protective conductors must be properly terminated at an accessory

▶ **Snag 27** **Earthing of time switches**

Time switches with metal parts must, in almost all cases, be earthed

▶ **Snag 28** **Suspended ceilings**

The metal parts of suspended ceilings do not, in general, need to be earthed or bonded

▶ **Snag 29** **Metal sinks**

Metal kitchen sinks do not require supplementary bonding

Earthing and Bonding   snags and solutions part 1

Earthing and Bonding   snags and solutions part 1

Bonding, not to be confused with Earthing

Equipotential bonding ('bonding' for short) is sometimes confused with earthing – even resulting occasionally in the use of the meaningless term 'earth bonding'.

Snag 1

It is easy to confuse earthing and bonding because of the visual similarities between them.

Green-and-yellow colour identification of the protective conductors is used for both, for example.

Both are associated with fault protection. However, bonding is quite distinct from earthing in its purpose, its general arrangement, and in many of the requirements of *BS 7671* that it has to satisfy.

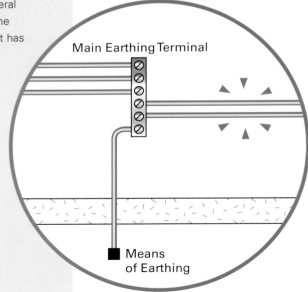

Main Earthing Terminal

Means
of Earthing

Solution

Earthing is intended to limit the duration of touch voltages, while bonding is intended to limit the magnitude of touch voltages.

The danger of electric shock due to earth fault conditions arises from the following voltages (sometimes called touch voltages) which may occur in an installation:

(a) voltages between exposed-conductive-parts and other exposed-conductive-parts

(b) voltages between extraneous-conductive-parts and other extraneous-conductive-parts

(c) voltages between exposed-conductive-parts and extraneous-conductive-parts

(d) voltages between exposed-conductive-parts and Earth, or extraneous-conductive-parts and Earth.

The purpose of earthing, where used for protective purposes within an installation, is to limit the duration of the voltages in (a), (b), (c) and (d) above. This is achieved by the operation of the relevant protective device (such as a fuse or circuit-breaker) under earth fault conditions, which removes the voltages by causing the automatic disconnection of the supply to the faulty circuit within the time specified in *BS 7671*.

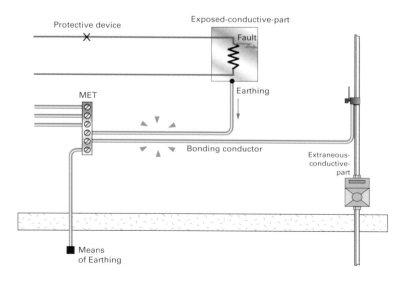

Without an adequate earthing arrangement, the protective device could not operate as required under earth fault conditions.

In contrast, the purpose of bonding is to limit the magnitude of the voltages in (a), (b) and (c). This is achieved by electrically connecting together those conductive parts.

The main safety benefit of adequate bonding is that the magnitude of voltages occurring between simultaneously accessible exposed-conductive-parts and extraneous-conductive-parts under earth fault conditions is insufficient to cause danger during the time taken for the relevant protective device to disconnect the supply to the faulty circuit.

The two main types of bonding recognized by *BS 7671* are main and supplementary.

- Main equipotential bonding is part of the protective measure Automatic Disconnection of Supply, which is used in virtually every electrical installation in the United Kingdom.
- Supplementary equipotential bonding provides additional protection in certain special installations or locations of increased shock risk such as those in Part 7 of *BS 7671*.

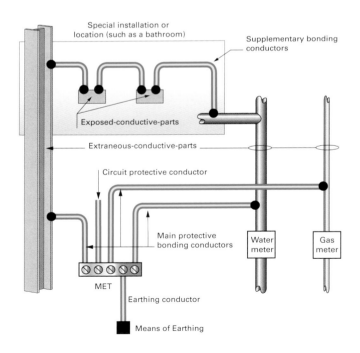

Each main bonding conductor connects one or more extraneous-conductive-parts to the Main Earthing Terminal (MET) of the installation. Supplementary bonding conductors, on the other hand, directly connect together all exposed-conductive-parts and all extraneous-conductive-parts and are not intended to be directly connected to the MET.

A by-product of equipotential (main and supplementary) bonding is that, under earth fault conditions, it may reduce the duration (not just magnitude) of the touch voltages in the installation. The reduction in touch voltage duration is related to the additional conductive paths that the bonding provides, which are in parallel with the earthing arrangement of the installation. The parallel paths allow a greater magnitude of earth fault current to flow, which reduces the time taken for the relevant protective device to automatically disconnect the supply to the faulty circuit, and consequently reduces the touch voltage duration.

Even so, bonding must **not** be relied upon to satisfy the disconnection time requirements of *BS 7671*, which is the function of earthing.

Both bonding and earthing must be provided in an installation, each to meet the respective safety requirements of *BS 7671*.

Definitions from *BS 7671*

Equipotential Bonding:
Electrical connection maintaining various exposed-conductive-parts and extraneous-conductive-parts at substantially the same potential

Earthing:
Connection of the exposed-conductive-parts of an installation to the main earthing terminal of that installation

Exposed-conductive-part:
Conductive part of equipment which can be touched and which is not normally live, but which may become live when basic insulation fails

Extraneous-conductive-part:
A conductive part liable to introduce a potential, generally earth potential, and not forming part of the electrical installation.

Electrical systems

Electrical systems and earthing
arrangements.

Snag 2

It is easy to incorrectly identify which
particular type of electrical system has
been installed. (For example TN-S, TN-C-S,
or TT).

The next few pages explain the different
electrical systems recognized by *BS 7671*
and briefly discuss their characteristics.

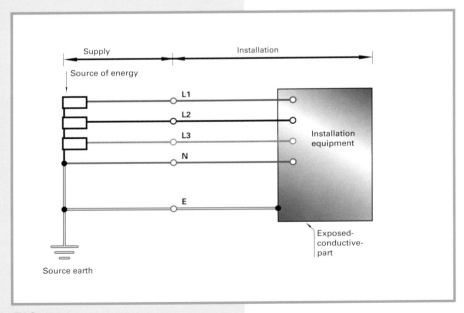

TN-S system

Solution

An electrical system consists of a single source of electrical energy and an installation. A source of energy may be, for example, a public supply network, a supply transformer, a private generator or a battery. An installation is an assembly of associated electrical equipment supplied from a common origin to fulfil a specific purpose and having certain co-ordinated characteristics. The type of system can generally be determined by examining the earthing arrangements at the origin of an installation.

The meaning of the letters is as follows:

The first letter relates to the source of energy (eg: a public supply network or a private generator).

T   denotes that one or more points of the source of energy are directly connected to Earth ('T' stands for 'Terra', or Earth).

I   denotes that all live parts are isolated from Earth or that the source of energy is connected to Earth through a deliberately introduced high earthing impedance ('I' stands for isolated).

The subsequent letters show the relationship between the protective and neutral conductors in the system and the method of earthing the installation.

The second letter refers to the installation earthing arrangements

T   denotes that the exposed-conductive-parts of the installation are directly connected to Earth.

N   denotes that the exposed-conductive-parts of the installation are directly connected to the earthed point of the source of energy. ('N' represents neutral or the equivalent point of the source in a d.c. system).

Subsequent letters indicate the system protective and neutral conductor arrangements

S   denotes that separate neutral and protective conductors are provided. ('S' stands for separate).

C   denotes that the neutral and protective functions are both performed by a single conductor, called a combined protective and neutral (PEN) conductor. ('C' stands for combined).

Electricity distributors sometimes use the term CNE (Combined Neutral and Earth), rather than PEN, for a combined protective and neutral conductor forming part of the distributors' conductors.

Types of system are identified by the letter code which indicates the relationship to Earth of the source of energy and of the exposed-conductive-parts of the installation as follows:-

TN System

A system having one or more points of the source of energy directly connected with Earth and having the exposed-conductive-parts of the installation connected to that point by protective conductors.

There are three types of TN system:

- The TN-S system, having separate neutral and protective conductors throughout the system.

  A TN-S system will most likely be met in practice in the form of an earth terminal provided by the electricity distributor which is connected to the cable sheath or to a separate overhead conductor.

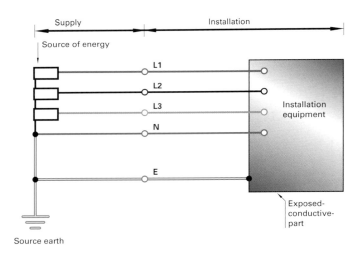

TN-S system

- The TN-C-S system, in which the neutral and protective functions are combined in a single conductor, the CNE (Combined Neutral and Earth) conductor or PEN conductor in part of the system.

The more common variant of TN-C-S, known as 'TN-C-S (PME)' is shown in Fig.1. This type of distribution is known as Protective Multiple Earthing (PME), and has been used by electricity distributors for most of the new low voltage supplies they have been installing since, the mid - 1970s. The Combined Neutral and Earth (CNE) conductor of the distributor's lines is connected to Earth at several points in accordance with Regulations 8.(3).(b) and 9(2) of *The Electricity Safety, Quality and Continuity Regulations 2002*, thereby providing low resistance connections between all parts of that conductor and Earth.

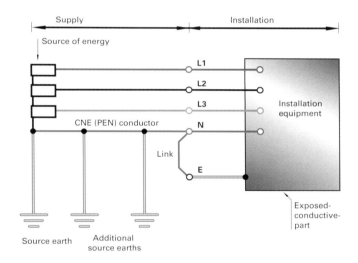

Fig.1 TN-C-S (PME) system

The other variant of TN-C-S, known as 'TN-C-S (PNB)'[1], is shown in Fig.2. This type of system may be used only where a single consumer is supplied from a distribution transformer (or other source such as a generating set). The CNE (or PEN) conductor is connected to Earth at one point only; this may be at the installation or closer to the source.

[1]PNB stands for Protective Neutral Bonding

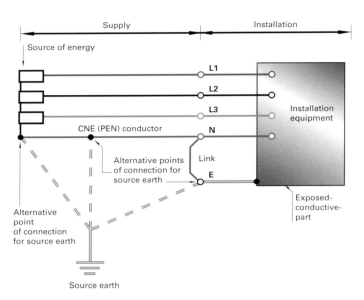

Fig.2 TN-C-S (PNB) system

- The TN-C system, in which the neutral and protective functions are combined in a single conductor throughout the system (ie both the source and the installation). TN-C systems are not permitted in consumer's installations.

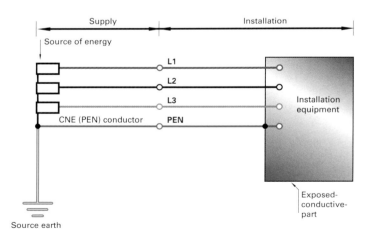

TN-C system

Earthing and Bonding

TT System

A system having one point of the source of energy directly connected with earth and having the exposed-conductive-parts of the installation connected to one or more installation earth electrodes electrically independent of the source earth electrode. This will be met in practice where the distributor does not provide an earth terminal or where, for one reason or another, it is not appropriate to earth the installation to such a terminal. The consumer must provide an earth terminal.

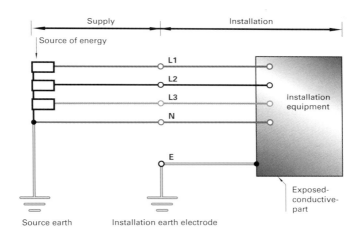

TT system

IT System

A system having no direct connection between the source of energy and earth but having the exposed-conductive-parts of the electrical installation being earthed.

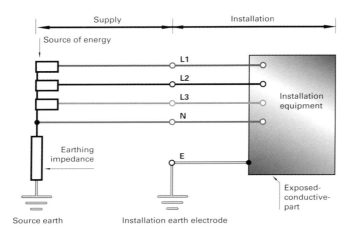

IT system

System: An electrical system consisting of a single source or multiple sources running in parallel of electrical energy and an installation. For certain purposes of the Regulations, types of system are identified as follows, depending upon the relationship of the source, and of exposed-conductive-parts of the installation, to Earth:

- **TN system**, a system having one or more points of the source of energy directly earthed, the exposed-conductive-parts of the installation being connected to that point by protective conductors,

- **TN-C system**, a system in which neutral and protective functions are combined in a single conductor throughout the system,

- **TN-S system**, a system having separate neutral and protective conductors throughout the system

- **TN-C-S system**, a system in which neutral and protective functions are combined in a single conductor in part of the system,

- **TT system**, a system having one point of the source of energy directly earthed, the exposed-conductive-parts of the installation being connected to earth electrodes electrically independent of the earth electrodes of the source,

- **IT System**, a system having no direct connection between live parts and Earth, the exposed-conductive-parts of the electrical installation being earthed.

Means of earthing in older installations

Older installations are sometimes found to employ the water service pipe as the sole means of earthing.

Snag 3

Older installations may use a gas, water or other metal service pipe as a means of earthing. **This is not permitted**.

It has never been permitted to use a gas pipe as a means of earthing and, since 1966, it has not been permitted to use any other service pipe either.

Necessary protective bonding connections **must** be made to the gas installation pipe, water and other metal service pipes.

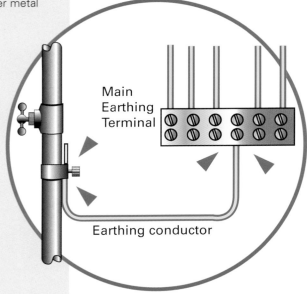

Main
Earthing
Terminal

Earthing conductor

Solution

Every electrical installation requires a proper means of earthing. This is normally realized by means of an electricity distributor's earthing terminal provided for this purpose near the electricity meter. If no such terminal is provided or is unsuitable, an earth electrode is required.

Although no metallic pipe for gases or other flammable liquids or the metallic pipework of a water utility service may be used as an earth electrode, other metallic water supply pipework may be utilized as an earth electrode where precautions are taken against its removal and it has been considered for such a use.

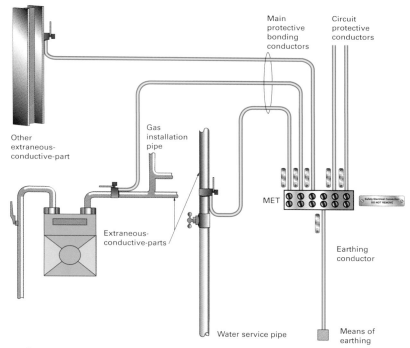

Main protective bonding conductors

Circuit protective conductors

Other extraneous-conductive-part

Gas installation pipe

Extraneous-conductive-parts

MET

Safety Electrical Connection
DO NOT REMOVE

Earthing conductor

Water service pipe

Means of earthing

Regulation 542.2.4

A metallic pipe for gases or flammable liquids shall not be used as an earth electrode. The metallic pipe of a water utility supply shall not be used as an earth electrode. Other metallic water supply pipework shall not be used as an earth electrode unless precautions are taken against its removal and it has been considered for such a use.

Cross-sectional area of the earthing conductor

The earthing conductor of an electrical installation is the protective conductor connecting the Main Earthing Terminal (MET) of the installation to the means of earthing. The cross-sectional area (csa) of the earthing conductor must meet the relevant requirements.

Snag 4

It is easy to incorrectly size the earthing conductor if account is not taken of one or more of the following factors:

- the electricity distributor's requirements,

- whether or not the conductor is buried,

- PME conditions, and

- in exceptional circumstances, where the earthing conductor is particularly long - as may be the case in a block of flats.

PME conditions

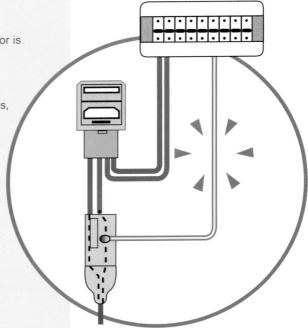

Solution

An incorrectly sized earthing conductor must be replaced with one having an adequate csa.

Permitted types of conductor

An earthing conductor normally consists of a single-core cable, a core of a multicore cable, or a tape or strip conductor. Other types of conductor, such as the metal sheath or armouring of a cable, or a metal conduit or structural steelwork, may be used as an earthing conductor providing the applicable requirements are met. Flexible or pliable conduit must not be selected as a protective conductor (Regulation 543.2.1 refers).

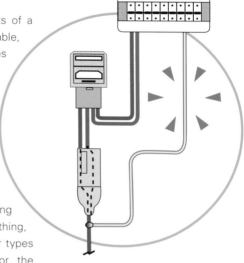

Where an electricity distributor's earthing facility is to be used as the means of earthing, the distributor may stipulate the type or types of conductor which may be used for the earthing conductor of an installation. Most electricity distributors publish notes of guidance which include their requirements regarding (amongst other things) permitted types of earthing conductor.

With certain exceptions, a protective conductor (including an earthing conductor) having a cross-sectional area (csa) of 10 mm^2 or less is required to be of copper (Regulation 543.2.3 refers).

Cross-sectional area

Subject to certain lower limits, the csa of an earthing conductor must be not less than a calculated value or a selected value (Regulations 543.1.1, 543.1.3 and 543.1.4 refer).

Generally, selection is the more commonly-used method for determining the required csa. Selection makes use of Table 54.7 of *BS 7671* together with knowledge of the csa and material of the associated line conductor.

Table 54.7 of *BS 7671*

Minimum cross-sectional area of protective conductor in relation to the cross-sectional area of associated line conductor

Cross-sectional area of line conductor	Minimum cross-sectional area of the corresponding protective conductor	
S	If the protective conductor is of the same material as the line conductor	If the protective conductor is not the same material as the line conductor
(mm^2)	(mm^2)	(mm^2)
S ≤ 16	S	$(k_1/k_2) \times S$
16 < S ≤ 35	16	$(k_1/k_2) \times 16$
S > 35	S/2	$(k_1/k_2) \times (S/2)$

where:

k_1 is the value of k for the line conductor, selected from Table 43.1 in Chapter 43 according to the materials of both conductor and insulation

k_2 is the value of k for the protective conductor, selected from Tables 54.2 to 54.6, as applicable.

Whether determined by calculation or selection, the csa of an earthing conductor must not be less than certain lower limits. For a copper earthing conductor which is not an integral part of a cable (such as a core of a cable) and not contained in an enclosure (such as conduit) formed by a wiring system, the csa must be not less than 2.5 mm^2 where protection against mechanical damage is provided, and 4 mm^2 where such protection is not provided (Regulation 543.1.1 refers).

Buried earthing conductor

Table 54.1 gives the minimum permitted csa for an earthing conductor embedded in the ground (Regulation 542.3.1 refers). The table is reproduced overleaf.

Table 54.1

snag **4**

Minimum cross-sectional area of a buried earthing conductor

	Protected against mechanical damage	Not protected against mechanical damage
Protected against corrosion by a sheath	2.5 mm^2 copper 10 mm^2 steel	16 mm^2 copper 16 mm^2 coated steel
Not protected against corrosion	25 mm^2 copper 50 mm^2 steel	

The requirements given in Table 54.1 are additional to those discussed earlier.

PME conditions

The earthing conductor of an installation which uses the earthing facility of a Protective Multiple Earthing (PME) supply as its means of earthing also performs the function of a main protective bonding conductor. Accordingly, the csa of the conductor must be not less than that determined in accordance with Regulation 544.1.1 for a main protective bonding conductor, or Section 543 for an earthing conductor, whichever is the greater.

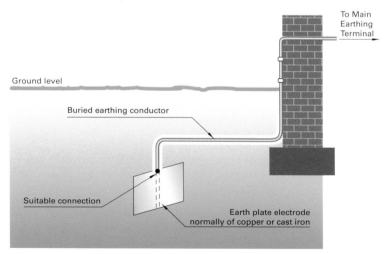

An earth plate electrode forming part of a TT system

Table 54.8

Minimum cross-sectional area of the main protective bonding conductor in relation to the neutral of the supply

NOTE: Local distributor's network conditions may require a larger conductor

Copper equivalent cross-sectional area of the supply neutral conductor	Minimum copper equivalent* cross-sectional area of the main protective bonding conductor
35 mm^2 or less	10 mm^2
over 35 mm^2 up to 50 mm^2	16 mm^2
over 50 mm^2 up to 95 mm^2	25 mm^2
over 95 mm^2 up to 150 mm^2	35 mm^2
over 150 mm^2	50 mm^2

* The minimum copper equivalent cross-sectional area is given by a copper bonding conductor of the tabulated cross-sectional area or a bonding conductor of another metal affording equivalent conductance.

Csa for fault protection

Exceptionally, the length of an earthing conductor may be such that its csa needs to be larger than that determined in accordance with Section 543 of *BS 7671*, in order to limit its end-to-end impedance. The impedance must not be so great as to cause the earth fault loop impedance (Z_s) of any circuit of an installation to exceed the maximum value permitted by Section 411 for fault protection.

For example, in a unit, such as a flat or suite of offices, forming part of a block of such units, the csa of an earthing conductor may need to be larger than that determined in accordance with Section 543. The distributor's earthing terminal may be situated at a group meter position some distance away within the block and, due to the length of the earthing conductor, its csa may need to be increased in order to limit its end-to-end impedance.

Regulation 542.3.1 (part of)

Every earthing conductor shall comply with Section 543 and, where PME conditions apply, shall meet the requirements of Regulation 544.1.1 for the cross-sectional area of a main protective bonding conductor. In addition, where buried in the ground, the earthing conductor shall have a cross-sectional area not less than that stated in Table 54.1. For a tape or strip conductor, the thickness shall be such as to withstand mechanical damage and corrosion (see *BS 7430*).

Regulation 543.1.1 (part of)

The cross-sectional area of every protective conductor, other than a protective bonding conductor, shall be:

(i) calculated in accordance with Regulation 543.1.3, or

(ii) selected in accordance with Regulation 543.1.4.

Regulation 543.2.1

A gas pipe, an oil pipe, flexible or pliable conduit, support wires or other flexible metallic parts, or constructional parts subject to mechanical stress in normal service, shall not be selected as a protective conductor.

Regulation 543.2.3

A protective conductor of the types described in items (i) to (iv) of Regulation 543.2.2 and of cross-sectional area 10 mm^2 or less, shall be of copper.

Regulation 544.1.1 (part of)

Except for highway power supplies and street furniture where PME conditions apply, the main protective bonding conductor shall be selected in accordance with the neutral conductor of the supply and Table 54.8.

Means of disconnection of the earthing conductor

A means of disconnection must be provided for the earthing conductor.

Snag 5

There can be a problem if a convenient and suitable means of disconnection has not been provided for the earthing conductor of an installation for test purposes.

Solution

A means for disconnection of the earthing conductor must be provided at or near the Main Earthing Terminal (MET) of an installation to facilitate measurement of the resistance of the earthing arrangements (Regulation 542.4.2 refers).

For larger installations, the requirements will often be met by providing a bolted link. For smaller, domestic installations, the earthing conductor will normally connect directly to the earthing bar in the consumer unit and disconnection will be effected by unscrewing and drawing back the earthing conductor.

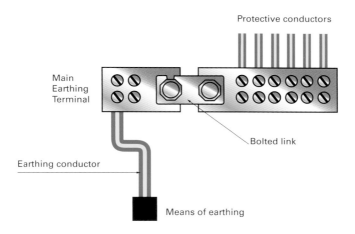

Regulation 542.4.2

To facilitate measurement of the resistance of the earthing arrangements, means shall be provided in an accessible position for disconnecting the earthing conductor. Such means may conveniently be combined with the main earthing terminal or bar. Any joint shall be capable of disconnection only by means of a tool.

Labelling of the earthing conductor

The earthing conductor, the conductor connecting the installation to the means of earthing, must be easily identifiable.

Snag 6

Earthing conductors are not always labelled where required making it easily possible to mistakenly disconnect the wrong conductor.

A main protective bonding conductor may unintentionally be disconnected when intending to disconnect the earthing conductor.

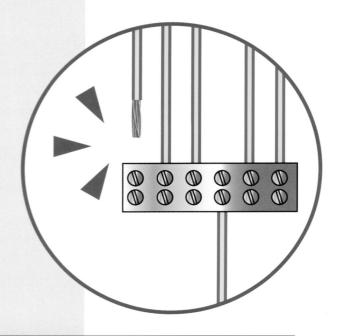

Earthing and Bonding

Solution

An earthing conductor comprising a single-core cable is required to be identified with the colour combination green-and-yellow (Regulation Groups 514.3 and 514.6 refer). A bare conductor (such as a tape or strip) used as an earthing conductor is required to be identified, where necessary, at intervals with the colour combination green-and-yellow (Regulation 514.4.2 refers).

In addition, like all the wiring of an installation, an earthing conductor is required, so far as reasonably practicable, to be so arranged or marked as to be identifiable for inspection, testing, repair and alteration of the installation (Regulation 514.1.2). In practice, an earthing conductor is often sufficiently identifiable due, for example, to its position or to the particular terminals to which it is connected. Otherwise, the function of the conductor must be indicated by labelling or other effective means.

Furthermore, a permanent label to *BS 951* with the words

Safety Electrical Connection - Do Not Remove

must be permanently fixed in a visible position at or near the point of connection of the earthing conductor to an earth electrode and the main earthing terminal where separate from main switchgear (Regulation 514.13.1 refers).

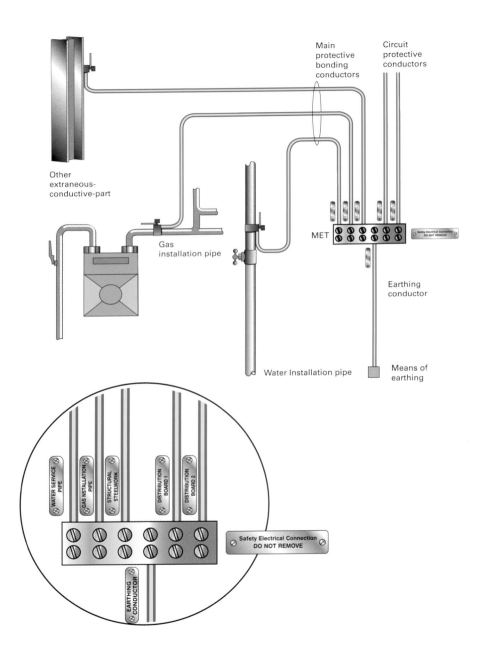

Main protective bonding conductors

Circuit protective conductors

Other extraneous-conductive-part

Gas installation pipe

MET

Safety Electrical Connection DO NOT REMOVE

Earthing conductor

Water Installation pipe

Means of earthing

WATER SERVICE PIPE

GAS INSTALLATION PIPE

STRUCTURAL STEELWORK

DISTRIBUTION BOARD 1

DISTRIBUTION BOARD 2

Safety Electrical Connection DO NOT REMOVE

EARTHING CONDUCTOR

Regulation 514.1.2

As far as is reasonably practicable, wiring shall be so arranged or marked that it can be identified for inspection, testing, repair or alteration of the installation.

Regulation 514.4.6

A bare conductor shall be identified, where necessary, by the application of tape, sleeve, or disc of the appropriate colour prescribed in Table 51, or by painting with such a colour.

Regulation 514.13.1

A permanent label to *BS 951* with the words "Safety Electrical Connection - Do Not Remove" shall be permanently fixed in a visible position at or near:

(i)   the point of connection of every earthing conductor to an earth electrode, and

(ii)   the point of connection of every bonding conductor to an extraneous-conductive-part, and

(iii) the main earth terminal, where separate from main switchgear.

Regulation 542.3.2

The connection of an earthing conductor to an earth electrode or other means of earthing shall be soundly made and be electrically and mechanically satisfactory, and labelled in accordance with Regulation 514.13.1. It shall be suitably protected against corrosion.

Protection of the earthing conductor against damage and deterioration

The earthing conductor, the conductor connecting the installation to the means of earthing, must be protected against damage. Its continuity must be assured throughout the life of the installation.

Snag 7

The earthing conductor of an electrical installation may sustain damage depending on where it is routed.

For example, with an installation forming part of a TT system, where the earthing conductor is routed outside, precautions may need to be taken to prevent it being crushed or broken by vehicles or livestock.

Furthermore, the earthing conductor may deteriorate over the lifetime of the installation due to external influences such as mechanical damage or corrosive substances.

Solution

No less than for any other part of an electrical installation, the earthing conductor and its electrical connections are required to be protected from any mechanical damage, corrosion or other external influences to which they may reasonably be expected to be exposed. *BS 7671* gives the main requirements relating to such protection in Regulation Group 543.3 (Preservation of electrical continuity of protective conductors), Section 522 (Selection and erection in relation to external influences) and Section 526 (Electrical connections).

Except where forming part of a multicore cable or where formed by conduit or trunking, an earthing conductor having a cross-sectional area (csa) of 6 mm^2 or less is required to be protected throughout its length by a covering at least equivalent to that of the insulation of a single-core non-sheathed cable of the appropriate size having a voltage rating of at least 450/750 V. (Regulation 543.3.2 refers). The same regulation requires an uninsulated protective conductor having a csa of 6 mm^2 or less, forming part of a cable, to be protected by prescribed insulating sleeving where the sheath of the cable is removed adjacent to joints and terminations.

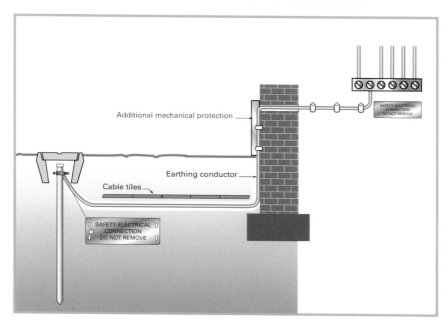

Additional mechanical protection

SAFETY ELECTRICAL CONNECTION DO NOT REMOVE

Earthing conductor

Cable tiles

SAFETY ELECTRICAL CONNECTION DO NOT REMOVE

Where an earthing conductor is liable to corrosion or mechanical damage its csa may need to be larger than that determined in accordance with Regulation 543.1.1, in order to protect the conductor against such influences (Regulation 543.3.1 refers). However, other means of protection such as enclosing the earthing conductor in conduit or trunking should also be considered. (Note: A ferrous conduit or trunking must not be used to enclose the earthing conductor unless the associated line and neutral conductors are also enclosed in the same conduit or trunking. See Regulation 521.5.2.)

The connection of an earthing conductor to an earth electrode must be suitably protected against corrosion (Regulation 542.3.2 refers).

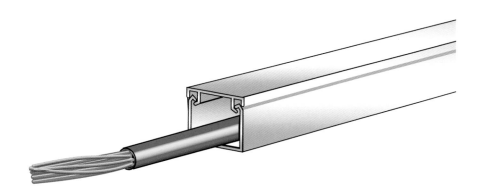

Earthing and Bonding   **snags and solutions** part 1

Regulation 521.5.2

Single-core cables armoured with steel wire or steel tape shall not be used for an a.c. circuit. The conductors of an a.c. circuit installed in a ferromagnetic enclosure shall be arranged so that all line conductors and the neutral conductor, if any, and the appropriate protective conductor are contained in the same enclosure.

Where such conductors enter a ferrous enclosure, they shall be arranged such that the conductors are only collectively surrounded by ferrous material.

Regulation 542.3.2

The connection of an earthing conductor to an earth electrode or other means of earthing shall be soundly made and be electrically and mechanically satisfactory, and labelled in accordance with Regulation 514.13.1. It shall be suitably protected against corrosion.

Regulation 543.3.1

A protective conductor shall be suitably protected against mechanical and chemical deterioration and electrodynamic effects.

Regulation 543.3.2

Excepting items (i) and (ii) below, a protective conductor having a cross-sectional area up to and including 6 mm^2 shall be protected throughout by a covering at least equivalent to that provided by the insulation of a single-core non-sheathed cable of appropriate size having a voltage rating of at least 450/750 V:

(i) a protective conductor forming part of a multicore cable

(ii) cable trunking or conduit used as a protective conductor.

Where the sheath of a cable incorporating an uninsulated protective conductor of cross-sectional area up to and including 6 mm^2 is removed adjacent to joints and terminations, the protective conductor shall be protected by insulated sleeving complying with *BS EN 60684* series.

Earthing clamps not to be used on cables

Earthing clamps must not to be used on paper-insulated/lead sheathed or steel wire armoured (swa) cables.

Snag 8

Under no circumstance should an earthing clamp (complying with *BS 951* or any other type) be attached to the lead sheath of any cable. In the case of a supply cable this practice is wrong for two reasons:

- the supply cable is the property of the electricity distributor and

- the securing of the clamp to the lead sheath is likely to damage the conductor insulation of the supply cable and, with the cold-flow of the lead, the connection is liable to loosen over time. *BS 951: 1999* states in Note 3 (second sentence) to its scope that 'such clamps are not intended for connection to the armour or sheath of a cable'.

In the worst cases, this practice may lead to increased risks from the hazards of fire or electric shock.

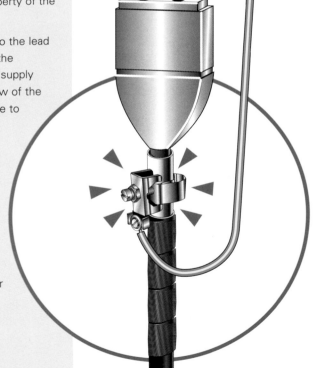

Solution

Many installations are supplied by paper-insulated/lead sheathed incoming service cables, and earthing facilities are often provided (by the distributor) by means of a wiped soldered joint on to the lead sheath, with an attached earth tail to an earthing block. However, there are many paper-insulated/lead sheathed supply cables that are not suitable for providing a connection to a means of earthing via the network distribution cables.

Where an adequate earthing facility has not been provided, electrical contractors are advised always to enquire of the cable owner (such as the electricity distributor) whether or not such a facility can be made available. It must never be assumed that, because a supply cable has a lead or other metallic sheath or armour, it is capable of providing an effective connection to Earth, or that it is adequate for carrying the prospective fault current.

The compressive forces exerted by tightening a clamp onto most types of armoured or metal sheathed cables (sufficient to provide a low resistance joint for fault or other currents to flow) are liable to cause damage to the conductor insulation and bedding. Such misuse of a clamp is a departure from Regulation 512.1.5.

One solution open to the installation designer is to make the installation part of a TT system.

Regulation 512.1.5

Every item of equipment shall be selected and erected so that it will neither cause harmful effects to other equipment nor impair the supply during normal service including switching operations.

Corrosion at earthing and bonding connections

Electrolytic action will result in corrosion at earthing and bonding connections.

Snag 9

Severe corrosion may be found only a few weeks after an aluminium label has been installed in contact with a clamp strap and a copper pipe.

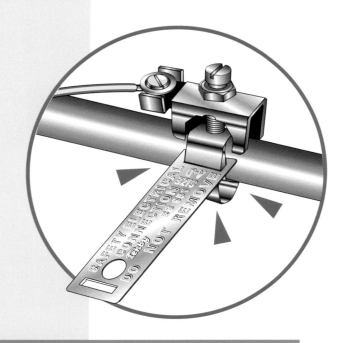

Solution

The aluminium warning label reading "Safety Electrical Earth - Do Not Remove" supplied with an earthing or bonding clamp to *BS 951* must not be installed in contact with a dissimilar metal (Regulation 522.5.2 refers). This is to avoid corrosion due to electrolytic action. Electrolytic action is a common problem with aluminium.

The label must be removed from the strap before attaching the clamp to the pipe.

The slots in the labels are intended only as an aid to packaging and storage. The label should be screwed to the clamp using the round hole.

Alternatively, the insulated protective conductor should be threaded through the round hole in the label in such a way that there is no contact between the label and other metals. Where a protective conductor is too large to pass through the holes, the label can still be attached to the protective conductor by using some smaller diameter insulated wire or insulated cable tie.

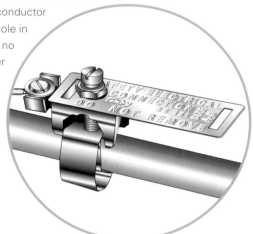

Regulation 522.5.2

Dissimilar metals liable to initiate electrolytic action shall not be placed in contact with each other, unless special arrangements are made to avoid the consequences of such contact.

Z_S values for TT systems

For a suitably designed installation forming part of a TT system, an earth electrode resistance not exceeding 200 Ω can, in many cases, be considered to be satisfactory.

Snag 10

For a TT system, it is unnecessary to obtain the Z_S values given in Tables 41.2, 41.3 and 41.4 of *BS 7671*, or the values printed on the inside covers of pads of NICEIC certificates and report forms, as these are **only** required for a TN system.

**LIMITING VALUES OF .
FOR COMMON OVERCURRENT PROTECTI
BASED ON 80% (APPR**

ated urrent (A)	Fuses				
	BS 88 (gG) Parts 2 and 6		BS 1361 or BS 1362		B:
	0.4 s	5 s	0.4 s	5 s	0.4 s
3	N/A	N/A	13.12	18.56	N/A
5	N/A	N/A	8.35	13.11	7.6
6	6.81	10.81	N/A	N/A	N
	4.08	5.93	N/A	N/A	
	N/A	N/A	1.94	3.06	
		N/A	2.63		

Solution

Information is given in both the Tables in Section 411 of *BS 7671* and also the table printed on the inside cover of pads of NICEIC certificates and report forms for values of earth fault loop impedance for fault protection, for overcurrent protective devices for **TN systems only**.

For a suitably designed installation forming part of a TT system, an earth electrode resistance not exceeding 200 Ω will be considered to be satisfactory (where earth fault protection is provided by an RCD) provided that the resistance value can be regarded as unlikely to change due to external influences (eg climatic conditions) and all applicable requirements including those in Regulations 411.5.1 to 411.5.4 are met.

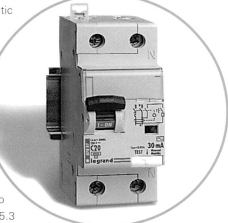

For an installation forming part of a TT system, Tables 41.2, 41.3, and 41.4 of *BS 7671* do not apply, and therefore the table on the inside covers of pads of NICEIC certificates and report forms do not apply either. The applicable requirements for a TT system include those expressed in Regulations 411.5.1 to 411.5.4. In particular, Regulation 411.5.3 requires that the following condition be satisfied:

Courtesy of Legrand Electric Ltd

$$R_A \cdot I_{\Delta n} \leq 50 \text{ V}$$

Where:

R_A is the sum of the resistances of the earth electrode and the protective conductor(s) connecting it to the exposed-conductive-part (Ω), and

$I_{\Delta n}$ is the rated residual operating current of the RCD.

To meet the condition in Regulation 411.5.3, in most cases installation designers

   Published by NICEIC. © Electrical Safety Council (JAN 2008) (3rd Ed.)

employ one or more residual current devices (RCDs) to provide additional protection against earth fault. In fact, Regulation 411.5.2 expresses a preference for the use of an RCD.

As an example, consider an installation forming part of a TT system where an RCD is selected as the device providing fault protection. Suppose that the RCD selected forms the main switch for the installation and has a residual operating current of 100 mA with a time-delayed characteristic. The reason for selecting such a time-delayed device, in this case, is to ensure discrimination with a 30 mA downstream device providing protection for a final circuit feeding socket-outlets where one or more of the socket-outlets is likely to supply portable equipment for use outdoors. Protection against overcurrent is provided, as normal, by devices such as circuit-breakers or fuses.

According to the above condition, an RCD with a rated residual operating current of 100 mA requires a maximum value of earth electrode resistance, R_A, of 500 Ω. These values are normally easily obtainable but, unless there are good reasons to expect such high values (such as hard/rocky ground conditions), Note 2 to Table 41.5 considers that an electrode with a measured value of R_A exceeding 200 Ω unstable and therefore unsuitable.

The factors affecting the resistance of an earth electrode include contact resistance, soil resistivity, the size and shape of the earth electrode and the depth of burying. Regulatory requirements applicable to earth electrodes are given in Regulation 542.2 of *BS 7671*.

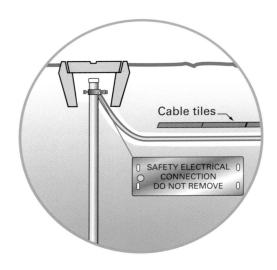

Cable tiles

SAFETY ELECTRICAL
CONNECTION
DO NOT REMOVE

Regulation 411.5.2

One or more of the following types of protective device shall be used, the former being preferred:

   (i)   an RCD

   (ii) an overcurrent protective device.

Regulation 411.5.3

Where an RCD is used for earth fault protection, the following conditions shall be fulfilled:

i) this disconnection time shall be that required by Regulation 411.3.2.2 or 411.3.2.4, and

ii) $$R_A . I_{\Delta n} \leq 50 \text{ V}$$

Where:

R_A is the sum of the resistances of the earth electrode and the protective conductor connecting it to the exposed-conductive-part (Ω),

$I_{\Delta n}$ is the rated residual operating current of the RCD.

Main equipotential bonding not provided

Older installations may be found not to include main equipotential bonding or to have main protective bonding conductors with cross-sectional area (csa) less than that required by *BS 7671*.

Snag 11

Electrical installations dating from the 1980s or before may have either:

- no main protective bonding conductors, or

- main protective bonding conductors with csa less than that required by the current edition of the Regulations.

Prior to 1966 the Wiring Regulations contained no requirements for main equipotential bonding.

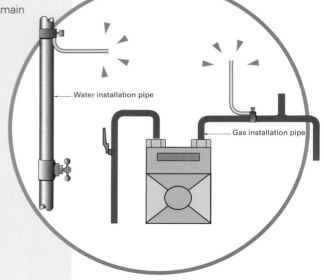

Water installation pipe

Gas installation pipe

Solution

Where fault protection is provided by Automatic Disconnection of Supply - as it is in most installations - the installation of main protective bonding conductors has, since 1966, been required. These protective conductors connect extraneous-conductive-parts such as water installation pipes, gas installation pipes, and certain other 'earthy' metalwork such as structural steelwork that may be present on the premises, to the Main Earthing Terminal.

During the 1980s new Regulations were introduced, requiring the minimum size of main protective bonding conductors to be larger than previously called for, particularly where there is a PME (protective multiple earthing) electricity supply.

For most dwellings the minimum size of main protective bonding conductor now permitted to be installed is 10 mm^2.

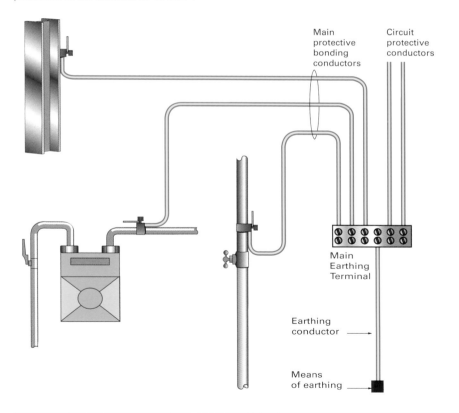

Regulation 411.3.1.2

In each installation main protective bonding conductors complying with Chapter 54 shall connect to the main earthing terminal extraneous-conductive-parts including the following:

(i) Water installation pipes

(ii) Gas installation pipes

(iii) Other installation pipework and ducting

(iv) Central heating and air conditioning systems

(v) Exposed metallic structural parts of the building.

Connection of a lightning protective system to the main protective bonding shall be made in accordance with *BS EN 62305*.

Where an installation serves more than one building the above requirement shall be applied to each building.

To comply with the requirements of these regulations it is also necessary to apply equipotential bonding to any metallic sheath of a telecommunication cable. However, the consent of the owner or operator of the cable shall be obtained.

Regulation 544.1.1

Except where PME conditions apply, a main protective bonding conductor shall have a cross-sectional area not less than half the cross-sectional area required for the earthing conductor of the installation and not less than 6 mm². The cross-sectional area need not exceed 25 mm² if the bonding conductor is of copper or a cross-sectional area affording equivalent conductance in other metals.

Except for highway power supplies and street furniture, where PME conditions apply, the main protective bonding conductor shall be selected in accordance with the neutral conductor of the supply and Table 54.8.

TABLE 54.8

Minimum cross-sectional area of the main protective bonding conductor in relation to the neutral of the supply

NOTE: Local distributor's network conditions may require a larger conductor.

Copper equivalent cross-sectional area of the supply neutral conductor	Minimum copper equivalent* cross-sectional area of the main protective bonding conductor
35 mm² or less	10 mm²
over 35 mm² up to 50 mm²	16 mm²
over 50 mm² up to 95 mm²	25 mm²
over 95 mm² up to 150 mm²	35 mm²
over 150 mm²	50 mm²

* The minimum copper equivalent cross-sectional area is given by a copper bonding conductor of the tabulated cross-sectional area or a bonding conductor of another metal affording equivalent conductance.

BS 951 Earthing and bonding clamps

Instances are observed of *BS 951* clamps not being used as intended.

Snag 12

Although *BS 951* specifies how and where such clamps may be used, NICEIC continually finds cases where they have been incorrectly installed or used inappropriately. Examples of such malpractice include:

- fitting a *BS 951* clamp to the armour or metallic sheath of a cable

- fitting a *BS 951* clamp that is unsuitable for the tube diameter

- linking two or more clamps to encircle a tube

- connecting clamps together by their straps

- use of unsuitable clamps in damp or corrosive conditions

- failure to fit a warning label

- warning label in contact with a dissimilar metal

- installing a clamp in an inaccessible location.

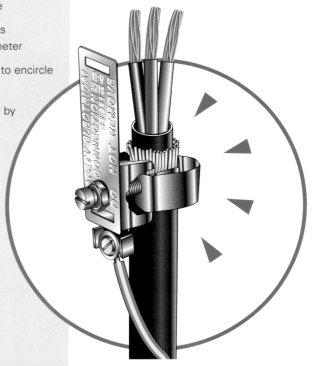

Earthing and Bonding

Solution

BS 951 specifies the performance and mechanical requirements for metal clamps that are used to provide mechanically and electrically sound earthing and bonding connections to metal tubes. The term 'tube' is to be taken to mean metal conduit, pipe or rod.

In order to comply with the relevant requirements of *BS 7671*, electrical contractors should always establish that the selected *BS 951* clamps are suitable for their intended application. Such clamps must therefore be appropriate for the metalwork to which the clamp is to be attached (having regard to the material, cross-section and dimensions); and the protective conductor which is to be connected to the clamp (having regard to the material, profile, number and shape of wires, and cross-sectional area).

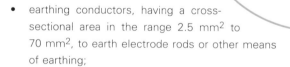

The scope of *BS 951: 1999* states that the clamps are primarily intended for use in electrical installations for the connection of:

- earthing conductors, having a cross-sectional area in the range 2.5 mm^2 to 70 mm^2, to earth electrode rods or other means of earthing;

- bonding conductors to metal tubes of circular cross-section that have circumferences of not less than 18.8 mm (ie diameters of not less than 6 mm).

Furthermore, *BS 951* clamps are designed to be used singly when encircling a tube and, where used, each clamp should be accompanied with a label to warn against its removal. The label must have a means of being securely fixed to either the clamp or the protective conductor, but not the strap, as corrosion due to electrolytic action, may occur. Note that the slots in the label are intended only to aid packaging and storage.

The arrangement for terminating a protective conductor to a clamp is separate from the means of tightening and locking the clamp for making electrical contact with the tube.

Depending on the manufacturer, the arrangement may be capable of accepting:

i) a conductor clamped under a screw head provided a captive washer is present so that the screw head does not act directly on the conductor, or

ii) a single conductor clamped directly by a screw-threaded arrangement, the cross-sectional area of the protective conductor being within the range specified within Table 1 of *BS 951*, or

iii) a bolted-on cable socket from a range of sockets that can accommodate conductors having cross-sectional areas covering the whole range specified within Table 1 of *BS 951*.

Clamps that utilize a terminating arrangement described in i) or ii) above should be marked in accordance with Table 1 of *BS 951*, as shown below. Additionally, such terminating arrangements provide for the looping in and out of an unbroken protective conductor.

The picture shows an example of how the reference system is used. In this instance, the words 'SIZE A–D' are stamped into the warning label, indicating the terminating arrangement of the associated clamp will accommodate a protective conductor having a cross-sectional area of between 2.5 mm^2 and 10.0 mm^2, inclusive.

The electrical connections between a *BS 951* clamp, the pipe to which it is attached, and the protective conductor connected to its termination arrangement must be accessible for inspection, testing and maintenance purposes. (Regulation 526.3 refers).

Table 1 of *BS 951: 1999* Termination reference and conductor size	
Termination reference	Nominal cross-sectional area of conductor (mm^2)
A	2.5
B	4
C	6
D	10
E	16
F	25
G	35
H	50
I	70

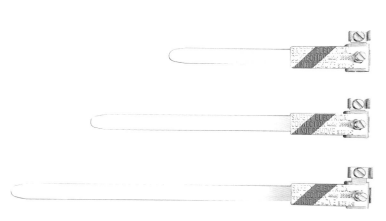

Courtesy of Tenby Industries Ltd

Regulation 526.1

Every connection between conductors or between a conductor and other equipment shall provide durable electrical continuity and adequate mechanical strength and protection. (Note: See Regulation 522.8 - Other mechanical stresses).

Regulation 526.3 (part of)

Every connection shall be accessible for inspection, testing and maintenance ...

Lightning protection systems

Lightning protection systems should be connected to the Main Earthing Terminal (MET).

Snag 13

Instances are occasionally encountered of lightning protection systems not connected to the Main Earthing Terminal of the electrical installation.

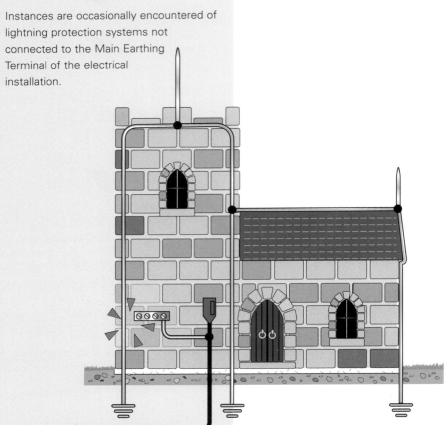

Solution

The lightning protection system must be connected to the MET of the electrical installation by main bonding conductor(s) complying with Section 544 (Regulation 411.3.1.2 refers).

Where there is a lightning protection system, due account must be taken of the recommendations of *BS EN 62305-3:2006 Protection against lightning* (Regulation 541.3 refers).

The lightning protection system itself is, however, excluded from the scope of *BS 7671* by Regulation 110.2.

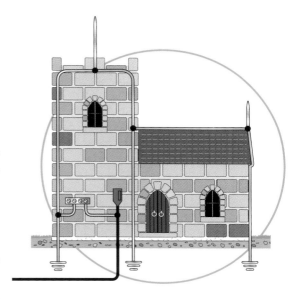

It is advisable that the exact positions of bonding connections are determined by the lightning protection system designer, due to the complexity of the requirements of *BS EN 62305-3*. Normally, the connection should be from the down conductor of the lightning protection system closest to the MET of the electrical installation, by the most direct route available. Bonding connections should not be made without consulting the designer of the lightning protection system, the system maintenance contractor or other competent person.

Bonding connections to a lightning protection system are normally made outdoors, and may involve conductors of different shapes and dissimilar metals. Accordingly, special consideration should be given to the requirement of Regulation 526.1 for electrical connections to provide durable electrical continuity and adequate mechanical strength, and those of Regulation Group 522.5 regarding measures to avoid corrosion.

Generally, the means of connection should be discussed and agreed with the lightning protection system designer and installer. It is often best for the actual making of a connection to the system to be to carried out by the lightning protection installer, although it is still the electrical contractor's responsibility to see that this is done satisfactorily.

Exceptionally, for reasons of safety, lightning protection system designers may advise that a main bonding connection should not be made to a lightning protection system. In such circumstances, the consequent departure from Regulation 411.3.1.2 must be recorded on the Electrical Installation Certificate and reference made to the last sentence of Regulation 120.3. The departure must be drawn to the customer's attention. This is permissible only where the electrical contractor has requested the main bonding connection be made, and has obtained the lightning protection system designer's written objection to the connection being made on grounds of safety.

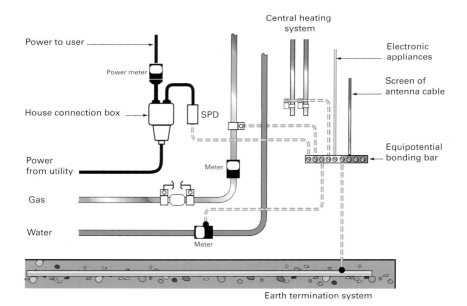

Earth termination system

Earthing and Bonding   snags and solutions part 1

Regulation 110.2 (part of)

The Regulations do not apply to the following installations:

(ix) Lightning protection systems for buildings and structures covered by *BS EN 62305*.

Regulation 120.3 (part of)

Any intended departure from these Parts requires special consideration by the designer of the installation and shall be noted on the Electrical Installation Certificate specified in Part 6.

Regulation 411.3.1.2 (part of)

In each installation main protective bonding conductors complying with Chapter 54 shall connect to the main earthing terminal extraneous-conductive-parts including the following:

(vi) Connection of a lightning protective system to the protective equipotential bonding shall be made in accordance with *BS EN 62305*.

Regulation 526.1

Every connection between conductors or between a conductor and other equipment shall provide durable electrical continuity and adequate mechanical strength and protection. (Note: See Regulation 522.8 - Other mechanical stresses).

Regulation 541.3

Where there is also a lightning protection system, reference shall be made to *BS EN 62305*.

Gas pipework

A main protective bonding conductor must be connected to the gas installation pipe.

Snag 14

Instances have been found of a main equipotential bonding connection being made to the gas service pipe and not the gas installation pipe.

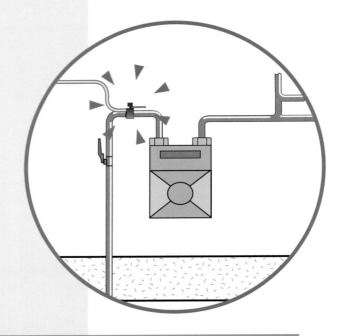

Solution

It is important to distinguish between the gas installation pipe, which is required to be bonded to the Main Earthing Terminal (MET) of the electrical installation, and the gas service pipe (Regulation 411.3.1.2 refers). A main equipotential bonding connection is required to be made to the gas **installation** pipe not the gas service pipe.

Note, however, that the definition of gas installation pipe given in Part 2 of *BS 7671* includes not only the pipework covered by the definition for gas installation pipework in *BS 6891: 2005 Installation of low pressure gas pipework up to 35 mm (R1 ¼) in domestic premises (2nd family gas)* specification (see over) but also a gas service pipe forming part of a primary meter installation. Where such a gas service pipe is routed within a consumer's premises in order to reach the primary meter and is of exposed metallic construction, main equipotential bonding of the pipe could be required by Regulation 411.3.1.2. However, a main equipotential bonding connection should not be made to a gas service pipe without the express written consent of the owner of that gas service pipe (eg Transco or another gas transporter). The owner may object on safety grounds, or for technical reasons such as the need to avoid electrolytic corrosion.

The main equipotential bonding connection must be made to the hard metal gas installation pipe, before any branch pipework, and, where practicable, within 600 mm of the meter outlet union (Regulation 544.1.2 refers).

Some metallic gas service pipes have a durable electrically-insulating coating (such as plastic) which completely covers the surface of the pipe. Main equipotential bonding of such pipes is generally not required by *BS 7671* (even where they traverse within consumers' premises), as they do not fall within the definition of an extraneous-conductive-part.

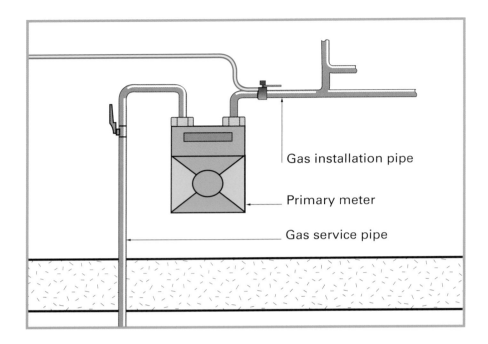

Gas installation pipe

Primary meter

Gas service pipe

Definitions

A definition of the term 'gas installation pipe' is given in Part 2 of *BS 7671*, as follows:

Any pipe, not being a service pipe (other than any part of a service pipe comprised in a primary meter installation) or a pipe comprised in a gas appliance, for conveying gas for a particular consumer and including any associated valve or other gas fitting.

Additionally, the two types of pipework are defined in *BS 6891: 2005*.

Installation pipework:

Pipework or fitting from the outlet of this meter installation to points at which appliances equipment are to be connected.

Service pipe:

Pipe for converging gas to premises from a distribution main, being any pipe between a distribution main and the outlet of the emergency control valve. (ECV).

Regulation 411.3.1.2 (part of)

In each installation main protective bonding conductors complying with Chapter 54 shall connect to the main earthing terminal extraneous-conductive-parts of that installation including the following:

    (ii) gas installation pipes.

Regulation 544.1.2

The main equipotential bonding connection to any gas, water or other service shall be made as near as practicable to the point of entry of that service into the premises. Where there is an insulating section or insert at that point, or there is a meter, the connection shall be made to the consumer's hard metal pipework and before any branch pipework. Where practicable the connection shall be made within 600 mm of the meter outlet union or at the point of entry to the building if the meter is external.

Semi-concealed gas meter boxes

A main equipotential bonding connection may need to be made to the gas installation pipe at a semi-concealed gas meter box.

Snag 15

Difficulties have been reported in finding a suitable place to connect a bonding conductor to the gas installation pipe where a semi-concealed gas meter box is employed.

It may not be practicable to provide a bonding connection at the point of entry to the premises in such a way as to make the connection accessible for inspection, testing and maintenance (Regulation 526.3).

A bonding connection to the gas installation pipework between the meter box and the premises may also be vulnerable to mechanical damage and/or corrosion and may not be advisable.

Solution

Where a semi-concealed meter box is fitted, the gas service pipe (as defined in *BS 6891: 2005 Installation of low pressure gas pipework up to 35 mm (R1 ¼) in domestic premises (2nd family gas)*) specification terminates at the meter, outside the premises. From the meter, the gas installation pipework (as defined) may then enter the premises at low level, such as below floor boards, or buried in concrete flooring or screed.

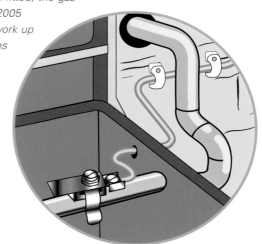

The connection of a main bonding conductor is to be made as near as practicable to the point of entry of a gas service into a premises (Regulation 544.1.2 refers). Furthermore, the connection must be made to the consumer's hard metal pipework before any branch pipework and, where practicable, within 600 mm of the meter outlet union or at the point of entry to the building if the meter is external.

It is generally preferable for a suitable bonding connection to be made inside the premises, but this may not always be practicable. In such situations, the most practical solution is often to make the bonding connection inside the meter box itself, by means of a *BS 951* earthing and bonding clamp of the appropriate size and cable capacity, fitted to the gas installation pipework where this is of the hard metal type.

The bonding conductor should be passed through the pre-drilled hole in the right-hand side of the meter box, and a "Safety Electrical Connection - Do Not Remove" label should also be attached (Regulation 514.13.1). Where a pre-drilled hole does not exist it is permitted for the bonding conductor to be installed with the gas pipe through an appropriately sealed sleeve. It is essential that the bonding conductor and its connection do not interfere with the integrity of the meter box.

The bonding conductor external to the box should be as short as possible before it passes through a hole in the external wall above the damp proof course. Like any other conductor, it should be properly supported by, for example, clipping to wall surfaces. The bonding conductor is permitted to run through the sleeve with the gas installation pipe, but it is essential that the sleeve is appropriately sealed with a non-setting, fire resistant compound, around both the installation pipework and the cable.

The bonding conductor should then be run back to the main earthing terminal of the electrical installation where it should be arranged or marked so that it can be identified for inspection, testing, repair or alteration of the installation in accordance with Regulation 514.1.2.

Certain older style semi-concealed gas meter boxes have an adaptor located in the side wall of the box. An earth tag washer is normally provided for connection of the bonding conductor, and a *BS 951* earthing and bonding clamp is not required. A label 'Safety Electrical Connection - Do Not Remove' should be attached.

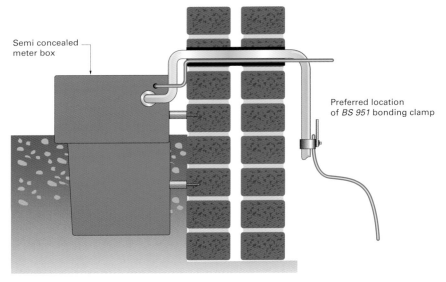

Semi concealed meter box

Preferred location of *BS 951* bonding clamp

Earthing and Bonding　　　**snags and solutions** part 1

Regulation 514.1.2

As far as is reasonably practicable, wiring shall be so arranged or marked that it can be identified for inspection, testing, repair or alteration of the installation.

Regulation 514.13.1

A permanent label to *BS 951* with the words "Safety Electrical Connection - Do Not Remove" shall be permanently fixed in a visible position at or near:

(i)   the point of connection of every earthing conductor to an earth electrode, and

(ii) the point of connection of every bonding conductor to an extraneous-conductive-part, and

(iii) the main earth terminal, where separate from main switchgear.

Regulation 526.3 (part of)

Every connection and joint shall be accessible for inspection, testing and maintenance, except for the following:

(ii) a compound-filled or encapsulated joint

(iii) a connection between a cold tail and the heating element as in ceiling heating, floor heating, or a trace heating system)

(iv) a joint made by welding, soldering, brazing or appropriate compression tool

(v)   a joint forming part of the equipment complying with the appropriate product standard.

Regulation 544.1.2

The main equipotential bonding connection to any gas, water or other service shall be made as near as practicable to the point of entry of that service into the premises. Where there is an insulating section or insert at that point, or there is a meter, the connection shall be made to the consumer's hard metal pipework and before any branch pipework. Where practicable the connection shall be made within 600 mm of the meter outlet union or at the point of entry to the building if the meter is external.

Main equipotential bonding in a block of flats

Main equipotential bonding must be provided in each flat in a block of flats.

Snag 16

NICEIC is occasionally asked whether main equipotential bonding should be provided for every flat in a block and, additionally, at the intake position.

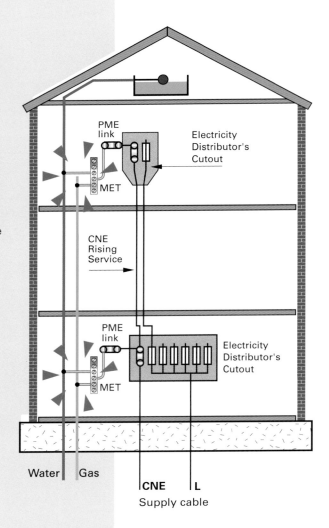

PME link

Electricity Distributor's Cutout

MET

CNE Rising Service

PME link

Electricity Distributor's Cutout

MET

CNE denotes combined neutral and earth conductor

Water   Gas

CNE   **L**

Supply cable

Solution

In each installation main protective bonding conductors must connect all the extraneous-conductive-parts to the Main Earthing Terminal (MET). (Regulation 411.3.1.2 refers). The requirements apply individually to each flat which has its own supply of electricity given in accordance with the *Electricity Safety, Quality and Continuity Regulations: 2002* (ESQCR). This is because the consumer's electrical equipment of each such separately-supplied unit (eg the consumer unit, wiring system and accessories) is an 'electrical installation' as defined in Part 2 of *BS 7671*.

Therefore, main bonding conductors complying with Section 544 are required to connect all the extraneous-conductive-parts within the flat to the MET. The main bonding connections to extraneous-conductive-parts such as gas, water, oil or other services need to be made as near as practicable to their points of entry to the respective flat, in accordance with the detailed requirements of Regulation 544.1.2.

The same requirements that apply to the installation of each separately-supplied flat also apply to the electrical installation in the common parts of the multi-occupancy premises (eg the landlord's areas). The extraneous-conductive-parts within such areas must be connected to the MET of that particular installation.

The supply arrangements may vary from those shown in the figure in a number of ways. For example, the meter operator's metering equipment may be grouped together at a common location, and/or the supplies may not be PME. The principles of application of Regulation 411.3.1.2, however, remain the same.

The electricity distributor may have particular requirements for main bonding, above and beyond those of *BS 7671*, especially where PME conditions apply. Most electricity distributors publish notes of guidance and/or drawings to explain any such requirements.

Definitions

Electrical installation. (abbr: Installation). An assembly of associated electrical equipment having co-ordinated characteristics to full specific purposes.

Origin of an installation. The position at which electrical energy is delivered to an electrical installation.

Earthing and Bonding

Regulation 411.3.1.2

In each installation main protective bonding conductors complying with Chapter 54 shall connect to the main earthing terminal extraneous-conductive-parts including the following:

(i) Water installation pipes

(ii) Gas installation pipes

(iii) Other installation pipework and ducting

(iv) Central heating and air conditioning systems

(v) Exposed metallic structural parts of the building

Connection of a lightning protection system to the protective equipotential bonding shall be made in accordance with *BS EN 62305*.

Where an installation serves more than one building the above requirements shall be applied to each building.

To comply with the requirements of these regulations it is also necessary to apply equipotential bonding to any metallic sheath of a telecommunication cable. However, the consent of the owner or operator of the cable shall be obtained.

Regulation 544.1.2

The main equipotential bonding connection to any gas, water or other service shall be made as near as practicable to the point of entry of that service into the premises. Where there is an insulating section or insert at that point, or there is a meter, the connection shall be made to the consumer's hard metal pipework and before any branch pipework. Where practicable the connection shall be made within 600 mm of the meter outlet union or at the point of entry to the building if the meter is external.

Re-emerging metallic pipework

Re-emerging metallic service pipework may need to be connected to the Main Earthing Terminal (MET) at the point at which it re-emerges.

Snag 17

In some installations, such as industrial premises, metallic pipework goes underground after the meter, and re-emerges in another location.

Such pipework may need to be connected to the main earthing terminal at the point at which it re-emerges, as well as at the point of entry into the premises.

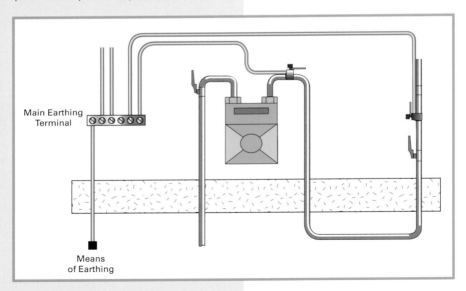

Main Earthing Terminal

Means of Earthing

Solution

A main equipotential bonding connection to any service pipework must be made as near as practicable to the point of entry of that service into the premises (Regulation 544.1.2 refers).

Such pipework may, after the intake position, go underground, become 'earthy' and re-emerge in another location in the premises.

There may be doubt concerning the reliability of the electrical continuity of such underground pipework. Where such pipework re-emerges, in almost all cases, it will meet the definition of an extraneous-conductive-part and must therefore be permanently and reliably connected to the MET in accordance with Regulation 411.3.1.2.

Regulation 411.3.1.2 (part of)

In each installation main protective bonding conductors complying with Chapter 54 shall connect to the main earthing terminal extraneous-conductive-parts including the following:

- (i) Water installation pipes
- (ii) Gas installation pipes
- (iii) Other installation pipework and ducting
- (iv) Central heating and air conditioning systems
- (v) Exposed metallic structural parts of the building

Connection of a lightning protection system to the protective equipotential bonding shall be made in accordance with *BS EN 62305*.

Where an installation serves more than one building the above requirements shall be applied to each building.

Regulation 544.1.2

The main equipotential bonding connection to any gas, water or other service shall be made as near as practicable to the point of entry of that service into the premises. Where there is an insulating section or insert at that point, or there is a meter, the connection shall be made to the consumer's hard metal pipework and before any point of entry to the building if the meter is external.

 Published by NICEIC. © Electrical Safety Council (JAN 2008) (3rd Ed.)

Earth continuity connections for metallic wiring systems

Suitable additional protective conductors may be required between adjacent sections of a metallic trunking system or other enclosure or support system for conductors, and between such a system and the equipment enclosure to which it connects.

Snag 18

Connections between adjacent lengths of metal trunking made by self-tapping screws or pop rivets may not provide reliable electrical continuity, adequate cross-sectional area (csa) and physical strength under normal and earth fault conditions (when a large current may flow in the trunking).

Solution

Every electrical connection is required to be protected against damage and deterioration. In addition, the connections are required to provide good metal-to-metal contact, be of adequate csa, and free from non-conductive coatings such as paint and of adequate mechanical strength.

The installation designer may decide that the connection needs to be supplemented by a suitable additional conductor, such as a copper cable or copper link, adequately electrically connected to the metalwork on either side and, where necessary, to the earthing terminals of the equipment concerned.

The metal trunking is required to comply with the requirements of *BS EN 50085*.

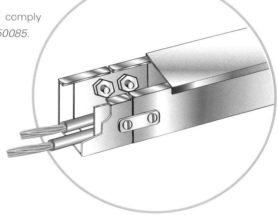

Regulation 526.1

Every connection between conductors or between a conductor and other equipment shall provide durable electrical continuity and adequate mechanical strength and protection. (Note: See Regulation 522.8 - Other mechanical stresses).

Regulation 543.2.5

The metal covering including the sheath (bare or insulated) of a cable, in particular the sheath of a mineral insulated cable, trunking and ducting for electrical purposes and metal conduit, may be used as a protective conductor for the associated circuit, if it satisfies both requirements of items (i) and (ii) of Regulation 543.2.4.

Metal lids of floor boxes

Metal lids of floor boxes will, in most circumstances, need to be earthed.

Snag 19

Floor boxes are often employed in open plan offices and showrooms to permit flexibility in the utilisation of the available space.

A floor box with a metal lid may inadvertently trap the flexible cord of the equipment which is plugged in.

Occurrences have been reported where the edge of the metal lid has cut into the sheath and the insulation of the cable with a risk of electric shock.

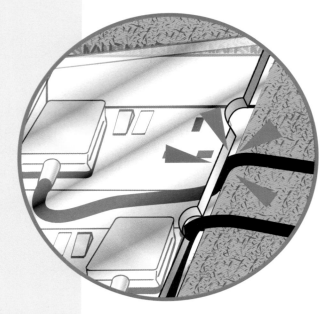

Solution

Users of the installation must take care not to trap or otherwise damage flexible cables and cords. Metal lids of floor boxes must be securely earthed with a short length of **flexible** protective conductor.

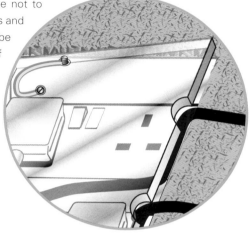

Regulation 411.4.2 (TN systems) (part of)

Each exposed-conductive-part of the installation shall be connected by a protective conductor to the main earthing terminal of the installation, which shall be connected to the earthed point of the power supply system.

Regulation 411.5.1 (TT systems)

Every exposed-conductive-part which is to be protected by a single protective device shall be connected, via the main earthing terminal, to a common earth electrode. However if two or more protective devices are in series, the exposed-conductive-parts may be connected to separate earth electrodes corresponding to each protective device.

For IT systems, see Regulation 411.6.2.

Electric towel rails

Supplementary bonding of an electric
towel rail in a location containing a bath or
shower may be provided by the circuit
protective conductor in the flexible cord.

Snag 20

A householder complained about the
unsightly appearance of many green-and-
yellow protective conductors and *BS 951*
clamps in his bathroom.

An unnecessary supplementary bonding
connection had been made to the
customer's recently installed electric
towel rail.

Solution

It is usually not necessary to provide an additional supplementary bonding conductor connecting the metal body of the electric towel rail directly to the remainder of the extraneous-conductive-parts and exposed-conductive-parts in zones 1 or 2 of the bathroom, even though in many cases a lug is provided. Where the location containing a bath or shower is in a building with a protective equipotential bonding system in accordance with Regulation 411.3.1.2 and where all the requirements of Regulation 701.415.2 are met supplementary bonding may be omitted. Where supplementary bonding is required, the circuit protective conductor in the flexible cord often meets the requirements of *BS 7671*. Supplementary bonding may have to be provided from the earthing terminal in the connection unit to other circuits and extraneous-conductive-parts in the bathroom if required by Regulation 701.415.2.

Regulation 544.2.5

Where supplementary bonding is to be applied to a fixed appliance which is supplied via a short length of flexible cord from an adjacent connection unit or other accessory, incorporating a flex outlet, the circuit protective conductor within the flexible cord shall be deemed to provide the supplementary bonding connection to the exposed-conductive-parts of the appliance, from the earthing terminal in the connection unit or other accessory.

Regulation 701.415.2 (part of)

Local supplementary equipotential bonding according to Regulation 415.2 shall be established connecting the protective conductor to the exposed-conductive-parts and accessible extraneous-conductive-parts within a room containing a bath or shower,...

Supplementary equipotential bonding may be erected outside or inside rooms containing a bath or shower, preferably close to the point of entry of extraneous-conductive parts into such rooms..

 Published by NICEIC. © Electrical Safety Council (JAN 2008) (3rd Ed.)

Earthing of metal back boxes

A suitable additional conductor, 'an earthing tail', may be required between an accessory and a flush-mounted metal back box to ensure that the metal back box is reliably earthed.

Snag 21

Where a metal back box has adjustable lugs, the reliability of the connection may be compromised.

During the lifetime of the installation, effects such as corrosion may result in a poor connection.

Under earth fault conditions, the circuit overcurrent protective device may fail to operate in the required time resulting in overheating and, under certain conditions, a risk of electric shock.

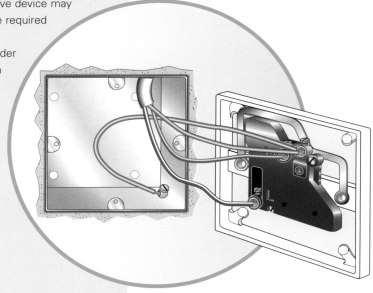

Solution

A metal back box for a **surface-mounted** accessory such as a socket-outlet is an exposed-conductive-part and a metal back box for a **flush-mounted** socket-outlet is **deemed** to be an exposed-conductive-part (even though it may not be able to be touched). Therefore, such back boxes, no less than every other exposed-conductive-part, are required to be earthed in accordance with Regulations 411.4.2 (TN systems) and 411.5.1 (TT systems).

Whether an earthing tail is required depends upon whether one or both of the lugs on the back box are adjustable (to permit the socket-outlet to be levelled) and upon the earthing strap and eyelet arrangement of the socket-outlet.

Should the installation designer decide that the reliability of the connection may not be assured throughout the lifetime of the installation, an earthing tail should be provided. An earthing tail consists of an additional protective conductor consisting of a length of suitably-sized and identified protective conductor connecting the earthing terminal of the socket-outlet with the earthing terminal of the metal back box.

Regulation 411.4.2 (TN systems) (part of)

Each exposed-conductive-part of the installation shall be connected by a protective conductor to the main earthing terminal of the installation, which shall be connected to the earthed point of the power supply system.

Regulation 411.5.1 (TT systems)

Every exposed-conductive-part which is to be protected by a single protective device shall be connected, via the main earthing terminal, to a common earth electrode. However if two or more protective devices are in series, the exposed-conductive-parts may be connected to separate earth electrodes corresponding to each protective device.

For IT systems, see Regulation 411.6.2.

Unused cores of multicore cables

It is advisable to properly terminate unused cores of a multicore cable.

Snag 22

If unused cores of multi-core cables are left "floating" in an enclosure, they may make contact with live parts resulting in the other end of the conductor becoming unexpectedly live.

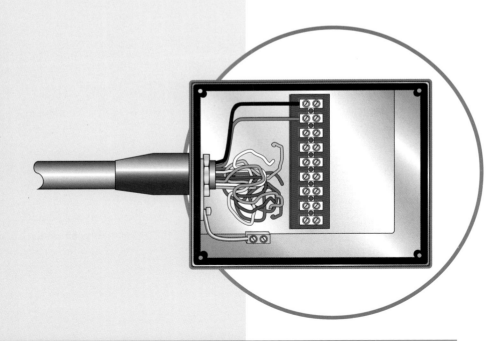

Earthing and Bonding

Solution

Although it is not strictly a circuit conductor, each unused core should be correctly terminated or insulated at both ends to eliminate the possibility of contact with a live terminal. This would 'protect against dangers that may arise from contact with live parts of the installation, as required by Regulation 131.2.1.

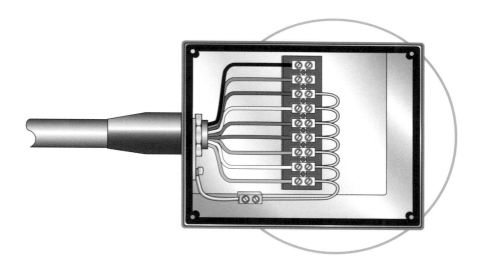

Regulation 131.2.1

Persons and livestock shall be protected against dangers that may arise from contact with live parts of the installation.

This protection can be achieved by one of the following methods:

   (i)   Preventing a current passing through the body of any person or any livestock

   (ii) Limiting the current which can pass through a body to a non-hazardous valve.

Damaged circuit protective conductors

Precautions must be taken so that cables are not damaged during installation.

Snag 23

A metallic floor box forming part of a ring final circuit in a car showroom was found during initial verification to be unearthed.

The two cables connecting to the floor box forming part of the ring final circuit had been 'pulled in' with such force that both circuit protective conductors (1.5 mm^2) had parted, but the live conductors (2.5 mm^2) remained intact.

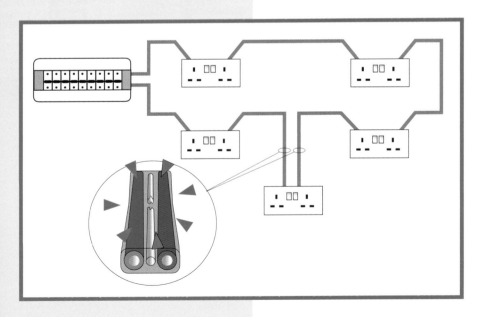

Solution

The cables were replaced and the necessary re-verification performed.

Care must be taken not to damage cables during installation (Regulation 522.8.1 refers). Insulated and sheathed cables (as any other cables) should only be pulled into a cable management system that will not cause damage to the cables.

Regulation 411.4.2 (TN systems) (part of)

Each exposed-conductive-part of the installation shall be connected by a protective conductor to the main earthing terminal of the installation, and that terminal shall be connected to the earthed point of the power supply system.

Regulation 411.5.1 (TT systems)

Every exposed-conductive-part which is to be protected by a single protective device shall be connected via the main earthing terminal, to a common earth electrode. However, if two or more protective devices are in series, the exposed-conductive-parts may be connected to separate earth electrodes corresponding to each protective device.

For IT systems, see Regulation 411.6.2.

Regulation 522.8.1

A wiring system shall be selected and erected to avoid during installation, use or maintenance, damage to the sheath or insulation of cables and and their terminations.

Unearthed sections of conduit

A single-phase lighting installation consisting of fibreglass and polycarbonate IP65 impact resistant, vandal resistant luminaires is connected by lengths of metal conduit.

Snag 24

Although a circuit protective conductor had been run to the earthing terminal of each luminaire, the sections of metal conduit between luminaires remained unearthed.

If earth continuity is not maintained and a fault develops in a conduit, due, for example, to mechanical damage or insulation failure of a live conductor, the metal conduit could attain line-to-earth voltage.

In such circumstances, the presence of the voltage is likely to remain undetected and pose a risk of injury to persons coming into contact with the conduit.

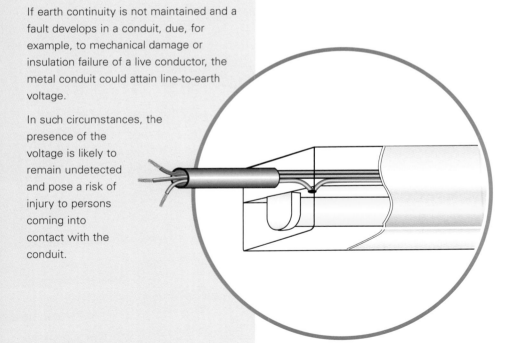

Solution

Where, as is usually the case, fault protection is provided by Automatic Disconnection of Supply, all exposed-conductive-parts of the installation must be earthed.

Installations comprising a mixture of metal and non-metallic enclosures, containment systems and/or wiring systems, require special care to be taken in design, construction, inspecting and testing, and in making alterations or additions, to ensure that all parts requiring to be earthed are, in fact, earthed effectively. Particular care is required where a metal containment or wiring system connects to non-metallic enclosures.

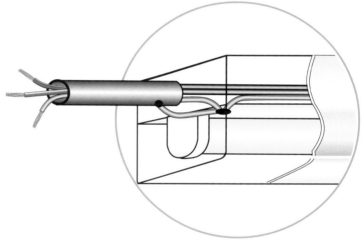

The installation designer must recognize the earthing problems that can occur when using non-metallic equipment enclosures and wiring systems, and make provision to overcome these at the design stage. Equally, it is important that the design is closely followed, so that all individual items that are required to be earthed are connected via protective conductors to the Main Earthing Terminal (MET) of the installation.

In almost every installation where unsheathed cables are used, metal enclosures and steel conduit systems will need to be effectively earthed. With metal wiring systems, the earthing of sections of conduit may be achieved by means such as bushes with earth tail connections, lock nuts or a proprietary clamp that attaches to the conduit permitting a suitable length of protective conductor to be connected. Protective conductors should then be suitably connected to ensure that all the sections of conduit and that the earthing terminal of each luminaire is connected to the MET.

Whether or not steel conduit is used as a circuit protective conductor, it is, in almost every case, required to be earthed. Even if a separate protective conductor is run in steel conduit, the conduit, being an exposed-conductive-part, will be required to be effectively and permanently connected to the circuit protective conductor(s) and hence to the MET.

However if sheathed cables are used it may not be necessary to earth the conduit.

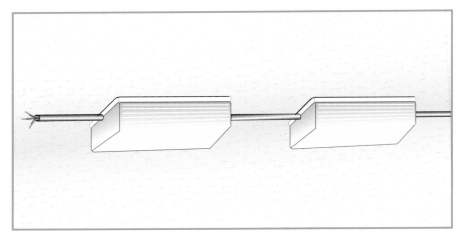

An alternative and better solution, at the design stage, is to avoid using luminaires as wiring ways. Luminaires may be mounted on conduit boxes so that modifications, such as rewiring or replacement of luminaires, can be made more easily.

Regulation 411.4.2 (TN systems) (part of)

Each exposed-conductive-part of the installation shall be connected by a protective conductor to the main earthing terminal of the installation, and that terminal shall be connected to the earthed point of the power supply system.

Regulation 411.5.1 (TT systems)

Every exposed-conductive-part which is to be protected by a single protective device shall be connected via the main earthing terminal, to a common earth electrode. However if two or more protective devices are in series, the exposed-conductive-parts may be connected to separate earth electrodes corresponding to each protective device.

For IT systems, see Regulation 411.6.2

Armour must be earthed

The armour of a steel wire armoured (swa) cable should always be earthed where fault protection is provided by the measure Automatic Disconnection of Supply.

Snag 25

Failure to adequately earth the armour of a swa cable may result in the protective device for the circuit not operating in the event of a fault to earth in the cable.

Failure to adequately earth the armour can occur, for example, where a swa cable is terminated at a non-metallic enclosure.

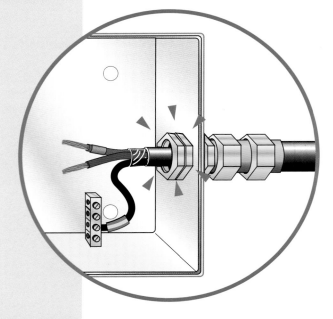

Earthing and Bonding

Solution

Where a steel wire armoured cable is selected for a wiring system, and if the applicable requirements such as the cross-sectional area (csa) being adequate can be met, the installation designer must decide whether to employ the armour as the circuit protective conductor.

- Where the armour is employed as the circuit protective conductor, the armour must be effectively earthed.

- Where the armour is not employed as the circuit protective conductor the swa cable may be selected with an additional core which is employed as the protective conductor. The armour should then be considered as an exposed-conductive-part and, once again, must be effectively earthed.

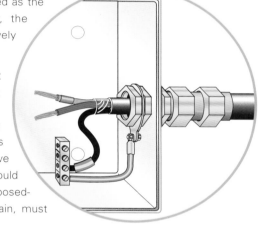

(Regulations 411.4.2 (TN systems) and 411.5.1 (TT systems) refer).

As for any other type of protective conductor, attention should be paid to the continuity and physical strength of electrical connections (Section 526), including the connection between the steel wire armouring and the cable gland and between the cable gland and other electrical equipment, such as an enclosure. For example, the gland must be the correct size and must firmly secure all the strands of the armour.

These connections are required to be protected against damage and deterioration. In addition, the connections are required to provide good metal-to-metal contact of adequate csa, free from non-conductive coatings such as paint. Alternatively, the connections must be supplemented by a suitable additional conductor, such as copper cable or copper tape, adequately electrically connected to the gland and to the earthing terminal of the electrical equipment concerned.

 Published by NICEIC. © Electrical Safety Council (JAN 2008) (3rd Ed.)

Furthermore, where the wire armouring of an swa cable is used as a protective conductor (Regulation 543.2.2 refers), it is subject to both of the following requirements (Regulations 543.2.4 and 543.2.5 refer):

- Its electrical continuity shall be assured, either by construction or by suitable connection, in such a way as to be protected against mechanical, chemical and electrochemical deterioration, and

- Its cross-sectional area shall be at least equal to that resulting from application of Regulation 543.1.

The armour of a steel wire armoured (swa) cable should always be earthed

Regulation 411.4.2 (TN systems)

Each exposed-conductive-part of the installation shall be connected by a protective conductor to the main earthing terminal of the installation, and that terminal shall be connected to the earthed point of the power supply system.

Regulation 411.5.1 (TT systems)

Every exposed-conductive-part which is to be protected by a single protective device shall be connected via the main earthing terminal, to a common earth electrode. However if two or more protective devices are in series, the exposed-conductive-parts may be connected to separate earth electrodes corresponding to each protective device.

For IT systems, see Regulation 411.6.2

Regulation 543.2.2 (part of)

A protective conductor may consist of one or more of the following:

(v) a metal covering, for example, the sheath, screen or armouring of a cable

Regulation 543.2.4

Where a metal enclosure or frame of a low voltage switchgear or controlgear assembly or busbar trunking system is used as a protective conductor, it shall satisfy the following three requirements:

(i) Its electrical continuity shall be assured, either by construction or by suitable connection, in such a way as to be protected against mechanical, chemical or electrochemical deterioration

(ii) Its cross-sectional area shall be at least equal to that resulting from the application of Regulation 543.1, or verified by test in accordance with *BS EN 60439-1*

(iii) It shall permit the connection of other protective conductors at every predetermined tap-off point.

Regulation 543.2.5

The metal covering including the sheath (bare or insulated) of a cable, in particular the sheath of a mineral insulated cable, trunking and ducting for electrical purposes, and metal conduit, may be used as a protective conductor for the associated circuit, if it satisfies both requirements of items (i) and (ii) of Regulation 543.2.4.

Protective conductor run to an accessory but not terminated

Protective conductors must be properly terminated at an accessory.

Snag 26

Protective conductors are not always terminated properly at accessories. For example, instances have been observed of the protective conductor having been either:

- cut off, or

- coiled in a loop and left.

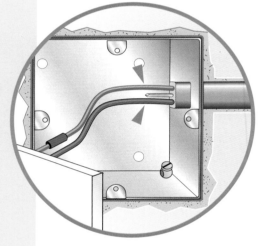

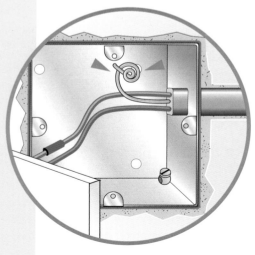

Solution

The protective conductor must be properly terminated as required by Regulation 411.3.1.1 and insulated sleeving provided as required by Regulation 543.3.2.

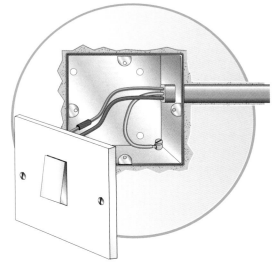

Regulation 411.3.1.1 (part of)

A circuit protective conductor shall be run to and terminated at each point in wiring and at each accessory except a lampholder having no exposed-conductive-parts and suspended from such a point.

Regulation 543.3.2 (part of)

Where the sheath of a cable incorporating an uninsulated protective conductor of cross-sectional area up to and including 6 mm^2 is removed adjacent to joints and terminations, the protective conductor shall be protected by insulating sleeving complying with *BS EN 60684* series.

Earthing of time switches

Time switches with metal parts must, in almost all cases, be earthed.

Snag 27

It is easy to overlook the presence of metal parts in time switches.

The consumer may need to make adjustments to the time switch settings, thereby making contact with metal parts such as the setting dial or levers and be at risk of electric shock.

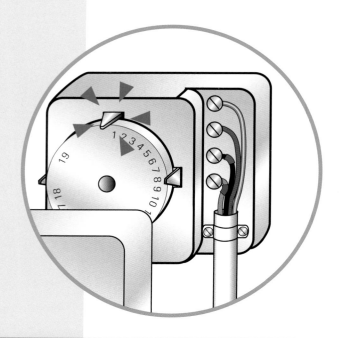

Solution

Almost all time switches, including those enclosed in all-insulated cases, are provided with an earthing terminal and are required to be earthed.

In installations where fault protection is provided by Automatic Disconnection of Supply, exposed-conductive-parts, such as the metallic mechanism of a time switch, must be effectively earthed. Unless metal parts of the time switch are separated from live parts by double insulation, connection to the protective conductor is essential for compliance with Regulation 411.4.2 or 411.5.1.

A protective conductor must be provided and properly terminated at each accessory as required by Regulation 411.3.1.1.

Regulation 411.3.1.1 (part of)

A circuit protective conductor shall be run to and terminated at each point in wiring and at each accessory except a lampholder having no exposed-conductive-parts and suspended from such a point.

Regulation 411.4.2 (TN systems) (part of)

Each exposed-conductive-part of the installation shall be connected by a protective conductor to the main earthing terminal of the installation, which shall be connected to the earthed point of the power supply system.

Regulation 411.5.1 (TT systems)

Every exposed-conductive-part which is to be protected by a single protective device shall be connected via the main earthing terminal, to a common earth electrode. However if two or more protective devices are in series, the exposed-conductive-parts may be connected to separate earth electrodes corresponding to each protective device.

For IT systems, see Regulation 411.6.2.

Suspended ceilings

The metal parts of suspended ceilings do
not, in general, need to be earthed or
bonded.

Snag 28

Electrical contractors sometimes provide
earthing and bonding to the metallic grid
of a suspended ceiling when it is not
necessary.

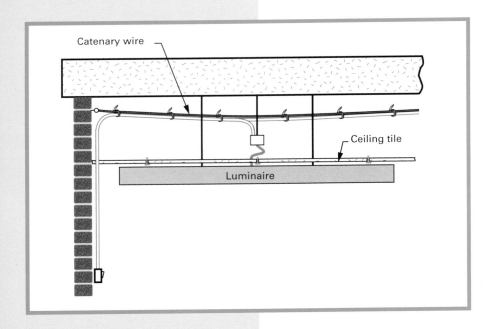

Catenary wire

Ceiling tile

Luminaire

Solution

In practice, unless there are very exceptional circumstances (which would need to be taken into account by the electrical designer), the conductive parts of a suspended ceiling will be neither exposed-conductive-parts nor extraneous-conductive-parts. Consequently, in normal circumstances, suspended ceilings need neither to be earthed nor equipotentially bonded.

Electrical equipment such as luminaires, lighting track, overhead busbars, air conditioning units and the like incorporated in a suspended ceiling will normally be of either Class I or Class II construction. The exposed-conductive-parts of Class I equipment are required to be connected to the main earthing terminal of the installation by a circuit protective conductor designed to conduct earth fault current. Class II equipment is designed such that any insulation fault in the equipment cannot result in fault current flowing into any conductive parts with which the equipment may be in contact. The conductive parts of a suspended ceiling incorporating Class I and/or Class II equipment are therefore not intended to conduct earth fault current, and so such parts need not be intentionally earthed. (Some conductive parts of a suspended ceiling may be earthed, however, by virtue of fortuitous contact with exposed-conductive-parts, including those of Class I equipment).

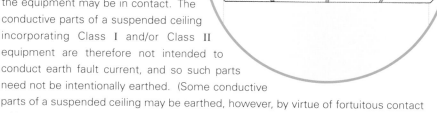

Unless there are exceptional circumstances, the conductive parts of a suspended ceiling will not introduce a potential that does not already exist in the space in which the ceiling is installed. In normal circumstances, therefore, there is no need to arrange for the conductive parts of the ceiling to be connected to either a main bonding conductor or to any supplementary bonding conductor.

The above principles also apply to metal parts of a suspended floor incorporating Class I or Class II equipment, such as in an office or computer room.

Snag 49, Extraneous-conductive-parts, discusses the definition of an extraneous-conductive-part.

Metal sinks

Metal kitchen sinks do not require
supplementary bonding

Snag 29

Does a metal kitchen sink, such as a
stainless steel sink, require
supplementary bonding?

Solution

Supplementary bonding to a metal kitchen sink is **not** required.

Supplementary bonding is required in certain locations of increased shock risk, such as those defined in Part 7 of *BS 7671* (swimming pools, agricultural and horticultural premises etc). A kitchen is not defined in *BS 7671* as a location of increased shock risk, hence supplementary bonding is not required.

Furthermore, a metal sink will almost certainly not be an extraneous-conductive-part in its own right (as defined in Part 2: Definitions of *BS 7671*), and therefore the need for main equipotential bonding is unlikely to arise.

An extraneous-conductive-part is defined in Part 2 of *BS 7671* as:

> *A conductive part liable to introduce a potential, generally earth potential, and not forming part of the electrical installation.*

A note in the *15th Edition of the IEE Wiring Regulation* stated that sinks might need to be bonded in areas where local supplementary bonding was provided. However such a note was not included in either the 16th Edition (*BS 7671*), or the 17th Edition (*BS 7671*).

Steel conduit systems

In installations employing a steel conduit wiring system, even if a separate protective conductor is run in the conduit, it is still necessary to (i) earth the conduit and (ii) ensure satisfactory continuity throughout the run.

Snag 30

The metal conduit could attain line-to-earth voltage if:

- the conduit is not connected to the Main Earthing Terminal (MET) and earth continuity is not maintained, and

- an earth fault develops in the wiring within the conduit (for example, due to mechanical damage or insulation failure).

In such circumstances, the presence of the voltage is likely to remain undetected and pose a risk of electric shock to persons coming into contact with the conduit.

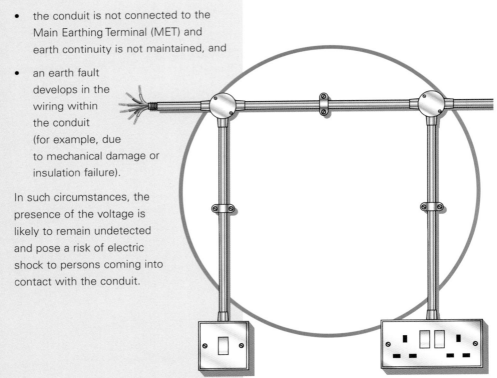

Solution

A steel conduit which contains unsheathed cables will meet the definition of an exposed-conductive-part and must be earthed to comply with Regulation 411.4.2 (for a TN system) or 411.5.1 (for a TT system).

Whether or not steel conduit is used as a circuit protective conductor (cpc), it is always required to provide reliable electrical continuity along its entire length. If a separate protective conductor is run in steel conduit, it is still necessary to earth the conduit. If a run of conduit is to be earthed at one point only, it must be ensured that there is satisfactory continuity throughout the run. If this is not done, each section of conduit would have to be connected to the internal protective conductor.

Conduit not used as a circuit protective conductor (cpc)

Where steel conduit is not used as a cpc, the conduit will, in almost all cases, be classed as an exposed-conductive-part and must therefore be connected by a protective conductor to the Main Earthing Terminal (MET) of the installation and must, throughout its length, comply with the relevant requirements of Regulation Group 411.

Conduit used as a protective conductor

Regulation 543.2.5 permits steel conduit to be used as a protective conductor for the associated circuit(s) provided it satisfies the requirements that the continuity of the steel conduit must be assured and the conduit must be of sufficient cross-sectional area (Regulation 543.2.4 refers).

Assembly of conduit systems

Further snags occasionally encountered with conduit wiring systems include:

Plain slip or pin grip socket joints are unlikely to provide reliable electrical continuity for the life of the installation. Note that in almost all circumstances all sections of conduit are required to be earthed, and this may prove unachievable if such joints are used.

The problem of loose, untightened conduit fittings, such as bushes, couplings and lock-nuts is occasionally encountered during installation inspections. Such loose fittings would result in poor or unreliable earthing of the conduit, and loss of electrical continuity. Continuity checks will not necessarily reveal such mechanical defects.

Continuity checks should always be supplemented by physical inspection.

Loose bushes are often found inside metal boxes where it is difficult to get an open-ended or adjustable spanner in to tighten the bush. Specially designed spanners are available for tightening such bushes. Loose couplings and lock nuts, where employed, should be tightened.

Paint or similar insulating material must be removed from the surface surrounding an entry and from any conduit coupler or similar fitting before terminating at a non-threaded entry. The paint serves more than just a decorative function - it is intended to prevent corrosion. Any 'bright metal' should be repainted immediately after assembly to ensure continuity is not subsequently lost due to oxidation. Sharp dies should be used when threading conduit to ensure good continuity.

Corrosion resistant finishes on steel conduit wiring systems, such as galvanizing or enamel paint, will suffer some damage during thread cutting and final assembly. Vice jaws and spanners may damage/remove the protective finish. The finish should be reinstated by the use of a cold galvanizing product or paint, as appropriate.

Regulation 411.4.2 (TN systems) (part of)

Each exposed-conductive-part of the installation shall be connected by a protective conductor to the main earthing terminal of the installation, which shall be connected to the earthed point of the power supply system.

Regulation 411.5.1 (TT systems)

Every exposed-conductive-part which is to be protected by a single protective device shall be connected via the main earthing terminal, to a common earth electrode. However if two or more protective devices are in series, the exposed-conductive-parts may be connected to separate earth electrodes corresponding to each protective device.

Regulation 543.2.4

Where a metal enclosure or frame of a low voltage switchgear or controlgear assembly or busbar trunking system is use as a protective conductor, it shall satisfy the following three requirements:

(i) Its electrical continuity shall be assured, either by construction or by suitable connection, in such a way as to be protected against mechanical, chemical or electrochemical deterioration

(ii) Its cross-sectional area shall be at least equal to that resulting from the application of Regulation 543.1, or, verified by test in accordance with *BS EN 60439-1*

(iii) It shall permit the connection of other protective conductors at every predetermined tap-off point.

Regulation 543.2.5

The metal covering including the sheath (bare or insulated) of a cable, in particular the sheath of a mineral insulated cable, trunking or ducting for electrical purposes and metal conduit, may be used as a protective conductor for the associated circuit, if it satisfies both requirements of items (i) and (ii) of Regulation 543.2.4.

Regulation 543.3.6

Every joint in metallic conduit shall be mechanically and electrically continuous.

Non-metallic enclosure

Where a steel conduit wiring system is interrupted by a non-metallic enclosure, continuity of the conduit must be ensured.

Snag 31

If a non-metallic enclosure is installed in a steel conduit system, and earth continuity is not provided across the insulated section, should a fault develop downstream the metal parts of that section of the installation could attain line voltage.

In such circumstances, the presence of the voltage may remain undetected and pose a risk of electric shock to persons coming into contact with the parts.

This situation can arise, for example, where an emergency stop switch or local isolator is installed in the supply to an electric motor.

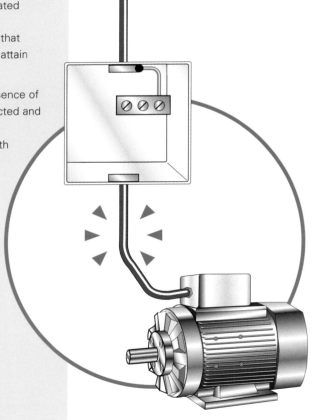

Solution

The steel conduit downstream of the non-metallic enclosure is, in almost all cases, likely to be an exposed-conductive-part and is required to be effectively earthed. (Regulations 411.4.2 and 411.5.1 refer).

Furthermore, it must not be forgotten that a circuit protective conductor (cpc) has to be run to, and terminated at, each point in wiring and at each accessory (except for certain lampholders). (Regulation 411.3.1.1 refers).

Protective conductors should be suitably connected to ensure that the downstream equipment and metal wiring system components are effectively earthed, and that the earthing terminal in any new accessory is also earthed.

The connections must meet all the applicable requirements, including those of Regulation 526.1.1 and Section 522 of *BS 7671*. Regulation 526.1 stipulates that all connections must provide durable electrical continuity and adequate mechanical strength and protection. Section 522 covers the requirements concerning selection and erection in relation to external influences.

The requirements are normally met with the aid of suitable connections to the earthing terminal in the non-metallic enclosure using lengths of protective conductor.

The non-metallic enclosure must have sufficient strength to permit termination of metallic wiring systems such as conduit without risk of damaging the enclosure, or compromising the overall robustness or degree of ingress protection of the system.

Any deficiencies resulting from omissions in design or construction should be identified and rectified during inspection and testing of the installation prior to energization. Continuity testing is required in accordance with Regulation 612.2.1 for all protective conductors up to the point of connection to all exposed-conductive-parts. Failure to adequately earth exposed-conductive-parts of the installation would put persons and/or livestock at risk of electric shock.

Earth continuity must be maintained where a metal wiring system such as a mineral insulated cable or a steel wire armoured cable is installed downstream of a non-metallic enclosure.

Finally, if a metal-bodied accessory is damaged and replaced by a non-metallic type, it is once again imperative that earth continuity be maintained.

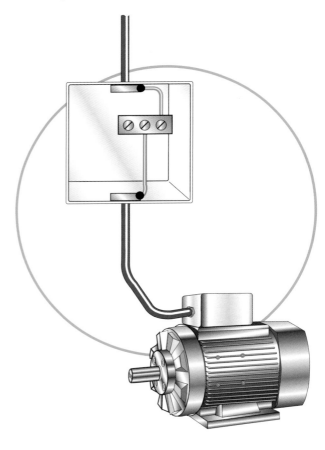

Earthing and Bonding   **snags and solutions** part 1

Regulation 411.3.1.1 (part of)

A circuit protective conductor shall be run to and terminated at each point in wiring and at each accessory except a lampholder having no exposed-conductive-parts and suspended from such a point.

Regulation 411.4.2 (TN systems) (part of)

Each exposed-conductive-part of the installation shall be connected by a protective conductor to the main earthing terminal of the installation, which shall be connected to the earthed point of the power supply system.

Regulation 411.5.1 (TT systems)

Every exposed-conductive-part which is to be protected by a single protective device shall be connected via the main earthing terminal, to a common earth electrode. However if two or more protective devices are in series, the exposed-conductive-parts may be connected to separate earth electrodes corresponding to each protective device.

For IT systems, see Regulation 411.6.2.

Regulation 612.2.1

A continuity test shall be made. It is recommended that the test be carried out with a supply having a no-load voltage between 4 V and 24 V, d.c. or a.c., and a short-circuit current of not less than 200 mA.

Main and supplementary bonding

Main and supplementary bonding conductors do not need to be interconnected.

Snag 32

Does *BS 7671* require a separate protective conductor to connect the supplementary equipotential bonding, in a location such as a swimming pool, with the Main Earthing Terminal and therefore the main equipotential bonding?

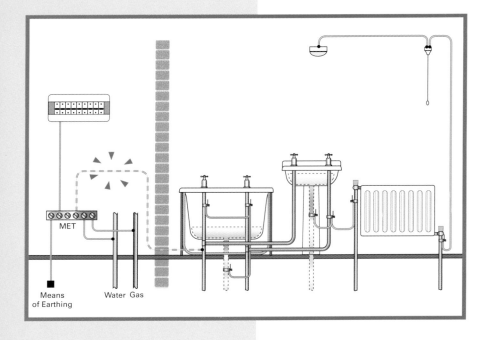

MET

Means
of Earthing

Water Gas

Solution

The answer is that such a protective conductor connection is **not** required by *BS 7671*.

However, in the particular case where the metal water installation pipe enters the installation in the location where additional protection by supplementary bonding is required and fault protection is provided by Automatic Disconnection of Supply, the pipe must be connected to the main equipotential bonding as required by Regulation 411.3.1.2. Furthermore, within the special location, the metal water installation pipe would meet the definition of an extraneous-conductive-part and would in almost all cases be subject to the requirements for supplementary bonding.

Regulation 411.3.1.2 (part of)

In each installation main protective bonding conductors complying with Chapter 54 shall connect to the main earthing terminal extraneous-conductive-parts of that installation including the following:

   i)   water installation pipes.

Regulation 702.411.3.3

All extraneous-conductive-parts in zones 0, 1 and 2 shall be connected by supplementary protective bonding conductors to the protective conductors of exposed-conductive-parts of equipment situated in these zones in accordance with Regulation 415.2.

Unsightly bonding clamps

Occasions have been observed of bonding clamps being removed by householders.

Snag 33

On occasions householders have been known to remove bonding clamps and cut back the supplementary bonding conductors because they look unsightly.

This situation is likely to be encountered in a bathroom where the clamps and supplementary bonding conductors are more visible.

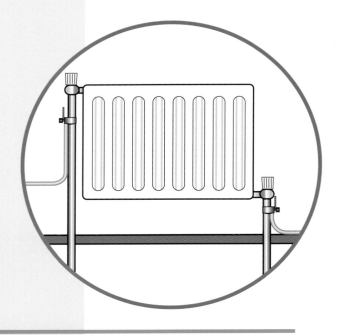

Solution

BS 951 clamps may not be visually pleasing to people. In most situations where bonding is required, the clamp normally can be installed out of sight, eg: under a basin, behind a panelled bath (where the panel is screwed in place but removable to permit access to the connection) or in an adjacent airing cupboard.

Because of the requirement of Regulation 701.415.2 for supplementary equipotential bonding to be established locally in a room containing a bath or shower, it may be necessary to provide a bonding connection to a radiator or towel rail forming part of a non-electrical central heating system. Where the plumbing of such a system employs pipework (eg: 15 mm diameter copper pipework) having metal-to-metal joints of negligible electrical impedance and of a permanent nature, it is usual to fix a bonding clamp to the radiator feed or return pipe. Because a BS 951 clamp employs screw connections, it must always be accessible for inspection. If the connection is made below the floor, a trap must be provided, marked and its position recorded and included in the information provided. The label required by Regulation 514.13.1 must be attached.

An alternative means of making a bonding connection 'out of sight' could, however, be employed as long as it satisfied Regulation 526.3. For example, the end of the supplementary bonding conductor could be securely soldered to the copper feed or return pipe (before filling with water) connected to the radiator, just below floorboard level where the pipe stubs project up to connect to the radiator valves. Means of access to inspect such a permanent means of connection is not required.

Regulation 514.13.1 (part of)

A permanent label to BS 951 with the words "Safety Electrical Connection - Do Not Remove" shall be permanently fixed in a visible position at or near:

(ii) the point of connection of every bonding conductor to an extraneous-conductive-part.

Regulation 526.3 (part of)

Every connection shall be accessible for inspection, testing and maintenance, except for the following:

(iv) a joint made by welding, soldering, brazing or appropriate compression tool.

Identification of protective conductors

Protective conductors must be properly identified and sleeved at terminations.

Snag 34

Two particular snags relating to the identification of circuit protective conductors (cpc) are:

- omission of sleeving at terminations of cables such as twin and cpc flat cables and three core and cpc flat cables, and

- the colour green (and not green-and-yellow) used to identify protective conductors.

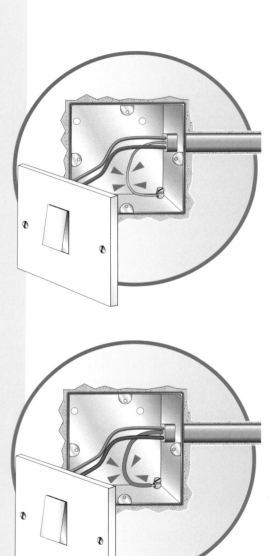

Solution

Green-and-yellow sleeving must be fitted at the
terminations of cables such as twin and cpc
flat cables to permit correct identification
of the conductor (Regulations 514.4.2,
514.4.4 and 514.4.5 refer), and to assist
in preserving the continuity of the
protective conductor (Regulation
543.3.2 refers).

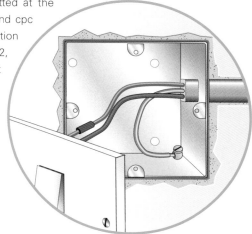

Regulation 514.4.2 (part of)

The bi-colour combination green-and-yellow shall be used exclusively for
identification of a protective conductor and this combination shall not be used for any
other purpose.

In this combination one of the colours shall cover at least 30 % and at most 70 % of
the surface being coloured, while the other colour shall cover the remainder of the
surface.

Regulation 514.4.5

The single colour green shall not be used.

Regulation 543.3.2 (part of)

Where the sheath of a cable incorporating an uninsulated protective conductor of
cross-sectional area up to and including 6 mm^2 is removed adjacent to joints and
terminations, the protective conductor shall be protected by insulating sleeving
complying with *BS EN 60684* series.

Supplementary bonding conductors

Older installations may not include supplementary bonding conductors.

Snag 35

Prior to 1981 there were virtually no requirements in the IEE Wiring Regulations for supplementary bonding conductors.

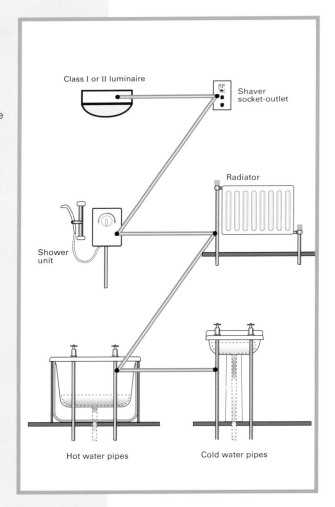

Class I or II luminaire

Shaver socket-outlet

Radiator

Shower unit

Hot water pipes

Cold water pipes

Solution

During the 1980s and 1990s the requirements for the sizing of supplementary bonding conductors were added to the IEE Wiring Regulations and subsequently amended.

Since 1981, the installation of supplementary bonding conductors has been required in installations and locations of increased electric shock risk, such as bathrooms and shower rooms (Section 701 refers). However, Regulation 701.415.2 permits supplementary equipotential bonding to be omitted where all of the following conditions are met.

(i) all final circuits of the location comply with the requirements for automatic disconnection according to 411.3.2 (where Table 41.1 requires a disconnection time of not more than 0.4 s in a TN system and 0.2 s in a TT system for a 230 V supply for final circuits not exceeding 32 A)

(ii) all final circuits of the location have additional protection by means of an RCD in accordance with 701.411.3.3, and

(iii) all extraneous-conductive-parts of the location are effectively connected to the protective equipotential bonding according to 411.3.1.2

For most dwellings the minimum size of supplementary bonding conductor is 4 mm^2, although 2.5 mm^2 can be used if the cable is mechanically protected against damage.

Regulation 415.2 (Note 1)

Supplementary equipotential bonding is considered as an addition to fault protection.

Regulation 701.415.2 (part of)

Local supplementary equipotential bonding according to Regulation 415.2 shall be established connecting together the terminals of the protective conductor of each circuit supplying Class I and Class II equipment to the accessible extraneous-conductive-parts , within a room containing a bath or shower, including the following:

(i) metallic pipes supplying services and metallic waste pipes (e.g. water, gas)

(ii) metallic central heating pipes and air conditioning systems

(iii) accessible metallic structural parts of the building; (metallic door architraves, window frames and similar parts are not considered to be extraneous-conductive-parts unless they are connected to metallic structural parts of the building)

Supplementary equipotential bonding may be installed outside or inside rooms containing a bath or shower, preferably close to the point of entry of extraneous-conductive-parts into such rooms.

Lighting circuits

Lighting circuits in older installations may not include circuit protective conductors.

Snag 36

Lighting circuits installed before 1966 often did not include a circuit protective conductor (cpc).

If Class I equipment, such as a metal luminaire (lighting fitting) switchplate or the like is subsequently installed, the addition of a circuit protective conductor is essential.

Without a cpc, there will be a risk of electric shock under fault conditions.

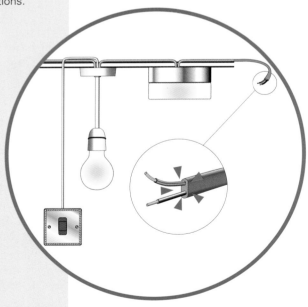

Earthing and Bonding

Solution

There is no legal requirement, and no regulation in *BS 7671*, requiring an existing lighting circuit to be rewired or otherwise upgraded to current standards.

Furthermore, it is permissible to extend or alter an existing lighting circuit having no cpc. However, the new work must be carried out in accordance with the current edition of *BS 7671*, and the safety of the existing installation must not be impaired.

The following are some of the main requirements of *BS 7671* that must be taken into account where an existing lighting circuit without cpc is to be extended or altered:

1. No alteration or addition may be made to an existing installation unless it has been ascertained that that the rating and condition of any existing equipment, including that of the distributor, which will have to carry the additional load is adequate for the altered circumstances and the earthing and bonding on which the alteration or addition will rely for safety is adequate (Regulation 131.8 refers). Amongst other things, the adequacy of the cross-sectional-area (csa) of the existing circuit conductors and the type and rating of the protective device must be established.

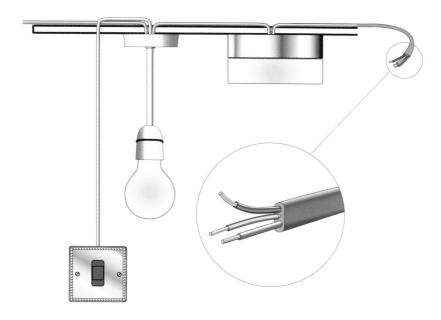

If, as is likely, protection against electric shock is provided by Automatic Disconnection of Supply, a cpc must be run to and terminated at each new point in wiring and at each new accessory (Regulation 411.3.1.1 refers).

2. A cpc must also be run to and terminated at any existing point in wiring or accessory that is changed from the all-insulated type to the type having metallic parts required to be earthed.

3. Furthermore, it is advisable that a cpc should be connected to any existing Class I equipment connected to the circuit if this equipment is not already satisfactorily earthed. Advice on dealing with existing Class I equipment that may not be earthed is given in a best practice guide entitled *Replacing a Consumer Unit in Domestic Premises Where Lighting Circuits Have No Protective Conductor*, published by the Electrical Safety Council. This may be downloaded from NICEIC Group Ltd at **www.niceicgroup.com**

4. Like a cpc used for any other purpose, a cpc installed to an existing point or accessory may consist of a separate green-yellow covered copper conductor. However, where a cpc is not an integral part of a cable (such as a twin and earth cable) and is not contained in an enclosure formed by a wiring system (such as trunking), it must have a cross-sectional area not less than:

    *   2.5 mm² if protection against mechanical damage is provided, or

    *   4 mm² if protection against mechanical damage is not provided
        (Regulations 543.1.1 and 543.3.1 refer).

5. Where a cpc consists of a separate green-yellow covered copper conductor, it must still be incorporated in the same wiring system as the live conductors or in their immediate proximity (Regulation 543.6.1 refers). This would require the cpc to be run along the same cable route(s) as the existing cables. The requirement does not apply where a residual current device is used for protection against electric shock.

In practice, rather than making changes to an existing lighting circuit having no cpc, the designer or contractor may persuade the customer that it would be safer and more practicable to rewire the circuit.

Regulation 131.8

No addition or alteration, temporary or permanent, shall be made to an existing installation, unless it has been ascertained that the rating and the condition of any existing equipment, including that of the distributor, will be adequate for the altered circumstances. Furthermore, the earthing and bonding arrangements, if necessary for the protective measure applied for the safety of the addition or alteration, shall be adequate.

Regulation 411.3.1.1 (part of)

A circuit protective conductor shall be run to and terminated at each point in wiring and at each accessory except a lampholder having no exposed-conductive-parts and suspended from such a point.

Regulation 543.1.1 (part of)

...the cross-sectional area shall be not less than 2.5 mm^2 copper equivalent if protection against mechanical damage is provided, and 4 mm^2 copper equivalent if mechanical protection is not provided.

Regulation 543.3.1

A protective conductor shall be suitably protected against mechanical and chemical deterioration and electrodynamic effects.

Regulation 543.6.1

Where overcurrent protective devices are used for fault protection against electric shock, the protective conductor shall be incorporated in the same wiring system as the live conductors or in their immediate proximity.

Main Earthing Terminal

A suitable Main Earthing Terminal (MET)
must be provided for every installation.

Snag 37

Snags commonly found at the main
earthing terminal of an installation include:

- An insufficient number of terminals
  being available

- Not all the terminals being suitable for
  the different-sized protective
  conductors that are to be, or have
  been, connected

- Terminals not being suitably marked,
  or arranged for identification

- The arrangement not being
  protected from external
  influences such as water,
  corrosion, damage or
  vandalism.

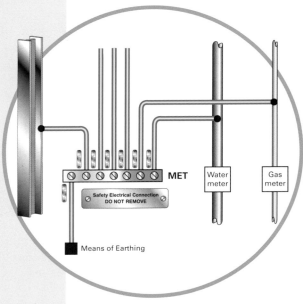

MET

Water
meter

Gas
meter

Safety Electrical Connection
DO NOT REMOVE

Means of Earthing

Solution

BS 7671 does not stipulate a particular form of MET, but leaves this to be dictated by the needs of the particular installation, subject to certain requirements being met. Hence METs take a variety of forms, ranging from simple to complex, either within or separate from the main switchgear.

The MET must be selected to take account of the following requirements:

- regulation 9 of the *Electricity at Work Regulations* requires that 'if a circuit conductor is connected to earth or to any other reference point, nothing which might reasonably be expected to give rise to danger by breaking the electrical continuity or introducing high impedance shall be placed in that conductor unless suitable precautions are taken to prevent that danger', and

- sufficient terminals are to be provided to accommodate separately the earthing conductor and all other conductors referred to in Regulation 542.4.1, not forgetting future additions that may reasonably be expected. Also sufficient terminals are required for the separate connection of any duplicate protective conductors required by Section 543.7 for circuits supplying equipment having high protective conductor currents, and

- the terminals are to be suitable for the conductor material, number and shape of wires, cross-sectional area and number of conductors to be connected together (for example for ring final circuits), and

- the effects of temperature and vibration are to be taken into account as required by Regulation 526.2, and

- the terminals are to be suitably arranged or marked so that the conductors connected to them can be identified for inspection, testing, repair or alteration of the installation as required by Regulation 514.1.2 (unless the conductors are identifiable by other means, such as markers attached to them), and

- a means for disconnecting the earthing conductor for testing is to be provided as required by Regulation 542.4.2, and

- where necessary, the MET and its connections need to be protected (eg by an enclosure) against vandalism, unauthorized interference or other external influences such as damp or dust, as required by Section 522, and

- where the MET is separate from the main switchgear, a permanent label, with the words 'SAFETY ELECTRICAL CONNECTION – DO NOT REMOVE', is to be fixed in a visible position at or near the MET, as required by Regulation 514.13.1.

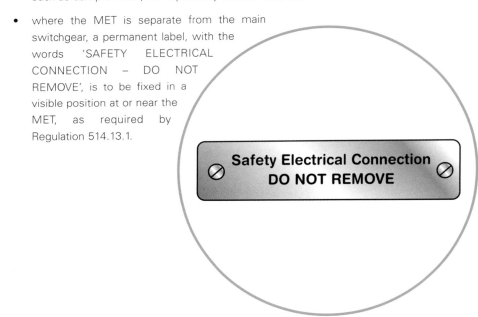

Safety Electrical Connection
DO NOT REMOVE

Earthing and Bonding　　　snags and solutions part 1

Regulation 514.1.2

As far as is reasonably practicable, wiring shall be so arranged or marked that it can be identified for inspection, testing, repair or alteration of the installation.

Regulation 514.13.1 (part of)

A permanent label to *BS 951* with the words "Safety Electrical Connection - Do Not Remove" shall be permanently fixed in a visible position at or near

(iii) the main earth terminal, where separate from main switchgear

Regulation 542.4.1

In every installation a main earthing terminal shall be provided to connect the following to the earthing conductor:

(i) The circuit protective conductors

(ii) The protective bonding conductors

(iii) Functional earthing conductors (if required)

(iv) Lightning protection system bonding conductor (if any).

Regulation 542.4.2

To facilitate measurement of the resistance of the earthing arrangements, means shall be provided in an accessible position for disconnecting the earthing conductor. Such means may conveniently be combined with the main earthing terminal or bar. Any joint shall be capable of disconnection only by means of a tool.

Earthing an electrical installation

Almost every installation needs to be effectively earthed to meet the requirements for safety.

Snag 38

Firstly, although it is the consumer's responsibility to ensure the installation is correctly earthed, in practice the electrical contractor, on behalf of the consumer, takes on this responsibility.

Secondly, an electrical installation contractor must not, under any circumstances, attempt to provide a means of earthing for an installation by attempting to clamp, sweat or in any other way connect the consumer's earthing conductor to the distributor's armouring or cable sheath. Such a connection to the armouring or cable sheath could result in an internal fault between the conductors of the cable, leading to injuries due to the explosive effects of arcing current and/or by any associated fire or flames.

The cable is the distributor's property and the contractor is not authorized to interfere with it.

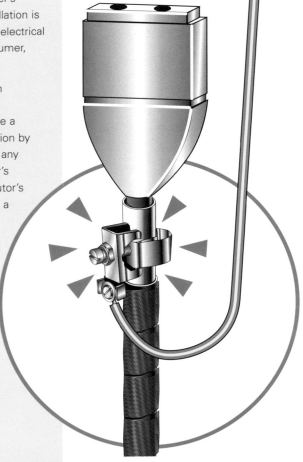

Solution

To ensure an electrical installation is effectively earthed,
the electrical contractor should:

- Establish at an early stage of the design of a new installation or an alteration or addition whether an earthing terminal for the consumer's use is already available at the service position.

- Where there is no such terminal, it should be ascertained whether the distributor is prepared to make one available.

- The effectiveness of any earthing terminal which does exist, and its connections to the distribution network, should be established. This should be done both by inspection and by measurement of the external earth fault loop impedance (Z_e). A safe method of measuring Z_e is explained in the NICEIC book entitled *Inspection, Testing and Certification*.

- For all installations, the type of earthing system needs to be established, and the appropriate arrangements need to be made for connecting the Main Earthing Terminal (MET) of the installation with Earth. For example, in a TN-S system, means must be provided for the MET to be connected to the earthed point of the source of energy (Regulation 542.1.2 refers). In a TN-C-S system where Protective Multiple Earthing (PME) is provided, means have to be provided for the MET to be connected by the distributor to the neutral of the source of energy (Regulation 542.1.3 refers).

- Where no earthing terminal is available at the service position and the distributor is not prepared to make one available, or the earthing terminal is unsuitable, the installation will need to be connected with Earth by its own electrically independent earth electrode (Regulation 542.1.4 refers). In such circumstances the requirements applicable to a TT system or an IT system have to be met.

- The metalwork of a gas, water utility other service pipe must not, in any circumstances, be used as an earth electrode for safety purposes in an installation. Other metallic water supply pipework shall not be used as an earth electrode unless precautions are taken against its removal and it has been considered for such use. However, this does not preclude the bonding of such metalwork where required by Regulation Group 411.3 (Regulation 542.2.4 refers).

- The electrical contractor should ensure that the installation is correctly earthed before issuing an Electrical Installation Certificate or, where applicable, a Domestic Electrical Installation Certificate.

New supply connection

An electricity distributor is obliged to provide an earthing terminal for the consumer's use in the case of a new supply connection at low voltage, except where this is inappropriate for safety reasons (regulation 24(4) of the *ESQCR* refers). For example, where PME (Protective Multiple Earthing) conditions apply, provision of an earthing terminal may be refused for installations in some types of premises. Most distributors publish notes of guidance advising on situations where an earthing terminal will not be provided.

Existing supply connection

A distributor is not obliged to provide an earthing terminal in the case of an existing supply connection, but may be willing to do so. Where an earthing terminal is provided, the distributor is responsible for ensuring that the terminal and its earthing connection to the distribution network are installed and, so far as reasonably practicable, maintained so as to prevent danger, and are suitable for the purpose (regulation 24(1) of the *ESQCR* refers). Nevertheless, the electrical contractor, on behalf of the consumer, must ensure that the earthing terminal is suitable for the requirements of the electrical installation and that it is properly connected to the main earthing terminal of the installation.

The Electricity Safety, Quality and Continuity Regulations 2002 (ESQCR)

Almost every installation needs to be effectively earthed to meet the requirements for safety. It is the consumer's responsibility to ensure the installation is correctly earthed. This is because, in order to receive a supply, the consumer is required to have an installation that meets the safety requirements of regulations 26(1) and 26(2) of the *ESQCR*.

The safety requirements of regulations 26(1) and 26(2) are that the consumer's installation is so constructed, installed, protected and used or arranged for use so as to prevent, so far as is reasonably practicable, danger or interference with the distributor's network or with supplies to others. A consumer's installation that complies with *BS 7671* is deemed to meet these requirements.

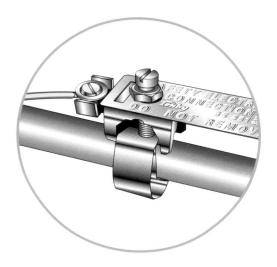

The metalwork of a gas, water utility other installation pipe must not, in any circumstances, be used as an earth electrode for safety purposes in an installation. Other metallic water supply pipework shall not be used as an earth electrode unless precautions are taken against its removal and it has been considered for such use.

Regulation 542.1.2

For a TN-S system, means shall be provided for the main earthing terminal of the installation to be connected with the earthed point of the source of energy. Part of the connection may be formed by the distributor's lines and equipment.

Regulation 542.1.3

For a TN-C-S system, where protective multiple earthing is provided, means shall be provided for the main earthing terminal of the installation to be connected by the distributor to the neutral of the source of energy.

Regulation 542.1.4

For a TT or IT system, the main earthing terminal shall be connected via an earthing conductor to an earth electrode complying with Regulation 542.2.

Regulation 542.2.4

A metallic pipe for gases or flammable liquids shall not be used as an earth electrode. The metallic pipe of a water utility supply shall not be used as an earth electrode. Other metallic water supply pipework shall not be used as an earth electrode unless precautions are taken against its removal and it has been considered for such a use.

Equipment in bathrooms

Local supplementary equipotential bonding in bathrooms must be established for new circuits in existing installations.

Snag 39

A problem often facing contractors is replacing equipment in locations containing a bath or a shower, at points where supplementary bonding has not been previously provided.

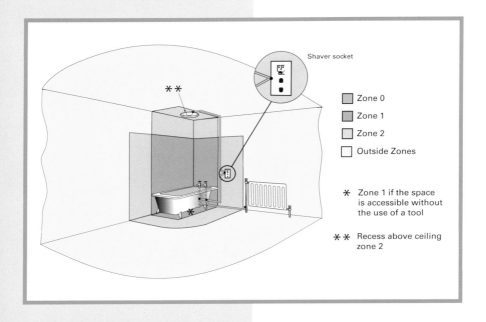

Shaver socket

Zone 0
Zone 1
Zone 2
Outside Zones

✳ Zone 1 if the space is accessible without the use of a tool

✳✳ Recess above ceiling zone 2

✳✳

✳

Solution

snag **39**

The 2001 amendment to *BS 7671* introduced a requirement for the terminal of the protective conductor of each circuit supplying Class I and Class II equipment in zones 1 or 2 to be included in the items to be connected together by local supplementary bonding. This requirement was intended primarily to make convenient provision, in a new installation, for a local supplementary bonding connection in case, during the life of the installation, any item of Class II equipment in a bathroom is replaced by an item of Class I equipment.

BS 7671: 2008 requires that in an existing bathroom where the maintenance of the electrical installation involves the replacement of an item of current-using equipment (such as a luminaire) with another similar item of current-using equipment, that local supplementary equipotential bonding according to Regulation 415.2 shall be established (Regulation 701.415.2 refers).

Regulation 701.415.2 does permit local supplementary equipotential bonding to be omitted where:

(i) All final circuits of the room containing a bath or shower comply with the requirements for automatic disconnection according to 411.3.2, and

(ii) All final circuits of the room containing the bath or shower have additional protection by means of an RCD in accordance with 701.411.3.3, and

(iii) All extraneous-conductive-parts of the location are effectively connected to the protective equipotential bonding according to 411.3.1.2.

Where local supplementary equipotential bonding does not exist refer to snag 53.

Regulation 701.415.2 (part of)

Local supplementary equipotential bonding according to Regulation 415.2 shall be established connecting together the terminals of the protective conductor of each circuit supplying Class I and Class II equipment to the accessible extraneous-conductive-parts , within a room containing a bath or shower including the following:

(i) metallic pipes supplying services and metallic waste pipes (e.g. water, gas)

(ii) metallic central heating pipes and air conditioning systems

(iii) accessible metallic structural parts of the building; (metallic door architraves, window frames and similar parts are not considered to be extraneous-conductive-parts unless they are connected to metallic structural parts of the building)

Supplementary equipotential bonding may be installed outside or inside rooms containing a bath or shower, preferably close to the point of entry of extraneous-conductive-parts into such rooms.

 Published by NICEIC. © Electrical Safety Council (JAN 2008) (3rd Ed.)

Alterations and additions

Alterations and additions must not be
made to an existing installation unless the
earthing and bonding arrangements are
adequate.

Snag 40

Unless earthing and bonding
arrangements are adequate, even a minor
alteration or addition cannot be made.

In an older installation where, for
example, the only means of earthing is
the water service pipe, the earthing and
bonding arrangements will have to be
upgraded to the current standard before
the alteration or addition can be made.

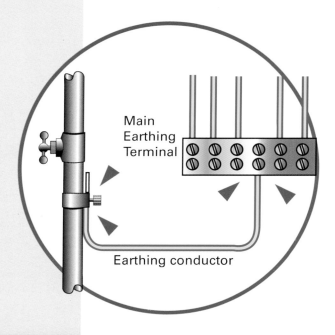

Main
Earthing
Terminal

Earthing conductor

Solution

Regulation 131.8 requires that no addition or alteration shall be made to an existing installation, unless it has been ascertained beforehand, amongst other things, that the earthing and bonding arrangements, if necessary for the protective measure applied for the safety of the addition or alteration, is adequate.

Therefore, the earthing arrangement for the addition or alteration (and, in practice, for the whole installation) must be one of those referred to in Regulations 542.1.1 to 542.1.4. The metalwork of a gas, water or other service is **not** permitted to be used for earthing (Regulation 542.2.4 refers).

NOTE: The use of a water service pipe as a means of earthing has been disallowed by the *IEE Wiring Regulations* for nearly 40 years because of the practice of water supply companies replacing metal water services pipes with electrically insulating ones. It has never been permitted to use a gas service as a means of earthing, because of the risk of explosion.

Regulation 131.8

No addition or alteration, temporary or permanent, shall be made to an existing installation, unless it has been ascertained that the rating and the condition of any existing equipment, including that of the distributor, will be adequate for the altered circumstances. Furthermore the earthing and bonding arrangements, if necessary for the protective measure applied for the safety of the addition or alteration, shall be adequate.

Regulation 542.2.4

A metallic pipe for gases or flammable liquids shall not be used as an earth electrode. The metallic pipe of a water utility supply shall not be used as an earth electrode. Other metallic water supply pipework shall not be used as an earth electrode unless precautions are taken against its removal and it has been considered for such a use.

Equipment connected by a socket-outlet

Like for like replacements are outside of the scope of *BS 7671*.

Snag 41

If an existing boiler is already connected to the electrical supply by a socket-outlet, and is to be replaced by a similar one, is it permitted to connect the new boiler in the same manner?

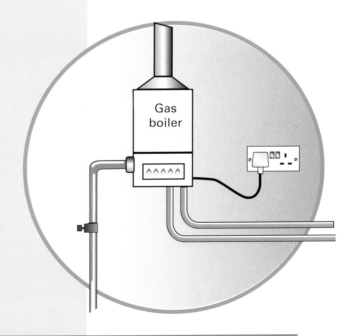

Earthing and Bonding

Solution

Yes.

A like-for-like replacement of an item of current-using equipment, such as a boiler, does not in itself constitute an alteration or addition to an electrical installation. The fixed electrical installation is not being altered or added to, and hence the requirements of *BS 7671* do not apply.

If the socket-outlet is physically damaged, or obviously unsuitable, then replacement should be recommended to the consumer. Essential inspection and testing should be carried out to ensure that, before being put into service, the replacement socket-outlet is safe to use. As a minimum, tests to confirm that shock protection has been provided are essential. These essential tests are earth fault loop impedance (the value of which needs to be checked against the characteristics of the protective device) polarity, and, where an RCD is provided, correct operation of the RCD. Where reasonably practicable, circuit resistance (R_1 and R_2, or R_2) and insulation resistance tests should be carried out. The measured values from such tests should be recorded.

Inadequate means of earthing

Action to be taken on discovering an installation without an adequate means of earthing.

Snag 42

Upon discovering an installation where the means of earthing is made to the water installation pipe, what action should be taken?

Should the installation be isolated, with the customers permission, or should the customer be informed that their installation is potentially dangerous?

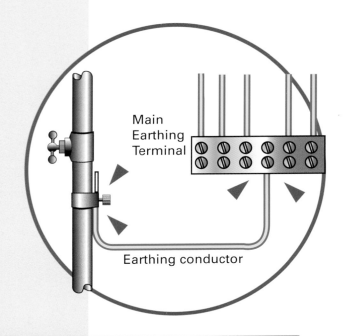

Main Earthing Terminal

Earthing conductor

Earthing and Bonding

Solution

Upon finding that an earthing arrangement does not meet the requirements of *BS 7671*, the electrical contractor should notify the customer of this in writing, without delay, giving a recommendation for remedial action (e.g. requires urgent attention).

As required by Regulation 131.8, no alteration or addition should be made to the existing electrical installation until the earthing and bonding arrangements are adequate.

Regulation 131.8

No addition or alteration, temporary or permanent, shall be made to an existing installation, unless it has been ascertained that the rating and the condition of any existing equipment, including that of the distributor, will be adequate for the altered circumstances. Furthermore, the earthing and bonding arrangements, if necessary for the protective measure applied for the safety of the addition or alteration, shall be adequate.

Looped main protective bonding conductors

Main protective bonding conductors should not be cut where looped between extraneous-conductive-parts.

Snag 43

Main protective bonding conductors should, ideally, not be looped from service to service.

If this is not practicable, the main protective bonding conductor should not be cut at looped connections.

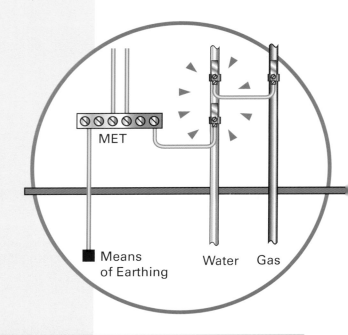

MET

Means
of Earthing

Water   Gas

Solution

Where a common bonding conductor loops in and out to connect to an extraneous-conductive-part, the protective conductor should be left unbroken at the connection. This is so that the continuity to other items connected to the bonding conductor will not be lost if the connection becomes detached (for example, as a result of work being carried out to pipework, see Regulation 528.3.3).

A permanent label bearing the words 'Safety Electrical Connection – Do Not Remove' is required in a visible position at or near the point of connection of every main bonding conductor to an extraneous-conductive-part, and at the main earthing terminal where this is separate from the main switchgear (Regulation 514.13.1 refers).

Regulation 514.13.1 (part of)

A permanent label to *BS 951* with the words "Safety Electrical Connection - Do Not Remove" shall be affixed in a visible position at or near:

> (ii) the point of connection of every bonding conductor to an extraneous-conductive-part.

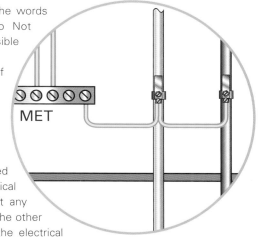

MET

Regulation 528.3.3

Where a wiring system is to be installed in proximity to one or more non-electrical services it shall be so arranged that any foreseeable operation carried out on the other services will not cause damage to the electrical service or the converse.

Locations containing a bath or a shower

Supplementary equipotential bonding is rarely required in a location containing a bath or shower.

Snag 44

In new premises it is required that all circuits are protected by an RCD.

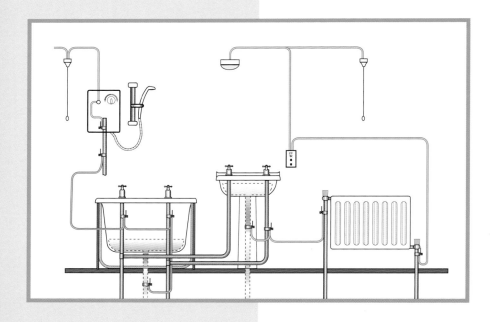

Solution

In locations containing a bath or shower, the risk of electric shock is increased due to a reduction in body resistance or by contact with earth potential. Where all the circuits in a location meet the disconnection requirements of Regulation 411.3.2, and all extraneous-conductive-parts of the location are effectively connected to the protective equipotential bonding according to 411.3.1.2, then the use of an RCD with a rated residual operating current $I_{\Delta n}$ of not more than 30 mA and a disconnection time of not more than 40 ms at a residual current of $5I_{\Delta n}$ for each of the circuits in the location will reduce the risk of death from an electric shock (Regulation 701.411.3.3 and Regulation 701.415.2 refer).

Under such conditions supplementary equipotential bonding will not be required.

Regulation 701.411.3.3 (part of)

Additional protection shall be provided for all circuits of the location, by use of one or more RCDs having characteristics specified in Regulation 415.1.1.

Regulation 701.415.2 (part of)

Where the location containing a bath or shower is in a building with a protective equipotential bonding system in accordance with Regulation 411.3.1.2, supplementary equipotential bonding to be omitted where all of the following conditions are met:

(i) All final circuits of the location comply with the requirements for automatic disconnection according to 411.3.2

(ii) All final circuits of the location have additional protection by means of an RCD in accordance with 701.411.3.3

(iii) All extraneous-conductive-parts of the location are effectively connected to the protective equipotential bonding according to 411.3.1.2.

Rooms containing a shower - other than a bathroom or a shower room

Bedrooms containing a shower cubicle are considered to be locations of increased shock risk and additional requirements for safety are placed in Section 701 of *BS 7671*.

Snag 45

Where a shower is installed in a bedroom, the requirements of *BS 7671*, including Section 701, must be applied.

Solution

The requirements of Section 701 of *BS 7671* apply to any location containing a bath or shower, and as such, the supplementary bonding requirements of Regulation 701.415.2 apply as well as the requirements of Regulation 701.411.3.3.

Socket-outlets may be installed in a bedroom containing a shower cubicle, and must therefore be installed at least 3 m from the edge of the shower basin or bath. All circuits must be protected by an RCD having a rated residual operating current of not more than 30 mA and capable of operating in 40 ms at a residual current $I_{\Delta n}$ of $5I_{\Delta n}$. (Regulation 701.411.3.3 refers).

Each item of electrical equipment in a location containing a bath, shower, and in a cabinet containing a shower and/or bath must be selected and erected so as to be suitable for the external influences likely to exist at the particular point of installation. Such influences are likely to include steam (leading to condensation), falling drops of water, and sprays and/or jets from shower nozzles. The suitability of electrical equipment for external influences in general is dealt with not in Section 701 but in the general requirements of *BS 7671* (see Regulation Group 512.2 and Section 522). Regulation 701.512.2 of Section 701 does however provide rules regarding the degree of protection against ingress of water into electrical equipment.

Schedule of zone definitions

The requirements for safety are based on a zonal concept, the requirements for each zone and beyond being based on the perceived degree of risk of electric shock. Regulation 701.32.1 divides locations containing baths or showers into three precisely-dimensioned zones designated zone 0, zone 1 and 2. The zones are determined taking account of walls, doors, fixed partitions, ceilings and floors, where these effectively limit the extent of a zone.

Zone 0 is the interior of the bath tub or shower basin. For showers without a basin, the height of zone 0 is 0.10 m and its surface extent has the same horizontal extent as zone 1.

Zone 1 is the three-dimensional space limited by the finished floor level and the horizontal plane corresponding to the highest fixed shower head or water outlet or the horizontal plane lying 2.25 m above the finished floor level, whichever is higher and the vertical plane circumscribing the bath tub or shower. For a shower without a basin, the limiting vertical plane of zone 1 is at a distance of 1.2 m from the centre point of the fixed water outlet on the wall or ceiling.

The space under that bath tub or shower basin is considered to be zone 1. However, spaces under the bath accessible only with the use of a tool are considered to be outside the zones.

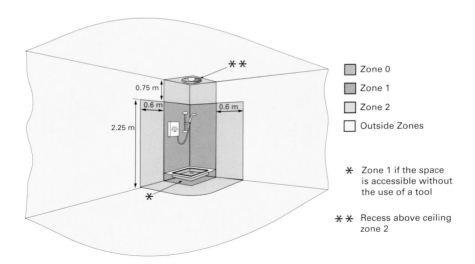

Earthing and Bonding

Zone 2 is the three-dimensional space limited by the finished floor level and the horizontal plane corresponding to the highest fixed shower head or water outlet or the horizontal plane lying 2.25 m above the finished floor level, whichever is higher and the vertical surface at the boundary of zone 1 and the parallel vertical surface at a distance of 0.60 m from the zone 1 border.

For showers without a basin, there is no zone 2 but an increased zone 1 is provided by the horizontal dimension or 1.20 m.

Regulation 701.411.3.3

Additional protection shall be provided for all circuits of the location, by the use of one or more RCDs having the characteristics specified in Regulation 415.1.1.

Regulation 701.415.2 (part of)

Local supplementary equipotential bonding according to Regulation 415.2 shall be established connecting together the terminals of the protective conductor of each circuit supplying Class I and Class II equipment to the accessible extraneous-conductive-parts, within a room containing a bath or shower, including the following:

(i) Metallic pipes supplying services and metallic waste pipes (e.g. water, gas)

(ii) Metallic central heating pipes and air conditioning systems

(iii) Accessible metallic structural parts of the building; (metallic door architraves, window frames and similar parts are not considered to be extraneous-conductive-parts unless they are connected to metallic structural parts of the building)

Supplementary equipotential bonding may be installed outside or inside rooms containing a bath or shower, preferably close to the point of entry of extraneous-conductive-parts into such rooms.

Bonding conductors

Bonding conductors must be properly
supported and protected.

Snag 46

In some instances a main or
supplementary protective bonding or
bonding conductor may have been
attached, for support, to a service such as
a water pipe.

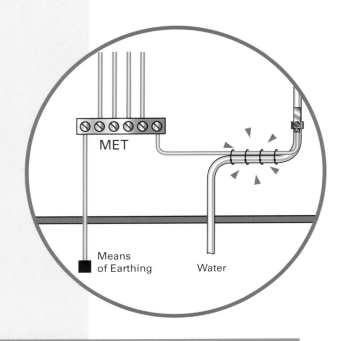

MET

Means
of Earthing

Water

Solution

As with all conductors, main protective bonding conductors and supplementary bonding conductors must be adequately supported without using non-electrical services, such as pipework, as a means of support (Regulation 528.3.3 refers).

Attention must also be paid to the ability of main bonding conductors to withstand external influences such as mechanical damage etc (Section 522), and any anticipated factors likely to result in deterioration (Regulation 543.3.1).

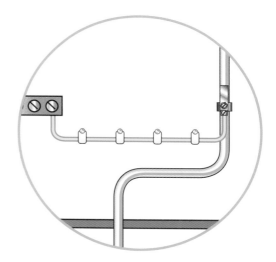

Regulation 528.3.3

Where an electrical service wiring system is to be installed in proximity to one or more non-electrical services it shall be so arranged that any foreseeable operation carried out on the other services will not cause damage to the electrical service or the converse.

Regulation 543.3.1

A protective conductor shall be suitably protected against mechanical and chemical deterioration and electrodynamic effects.

Main equipotential bonding - more than one building

Main equipotential bonding requirements where an installation serves more than one building.

Snag 47

Is main equipotential bonding ('main bonding', for short) required to metallic pipework which is common to separate buildings supplied by the same electrical installation, and if so, at which building?

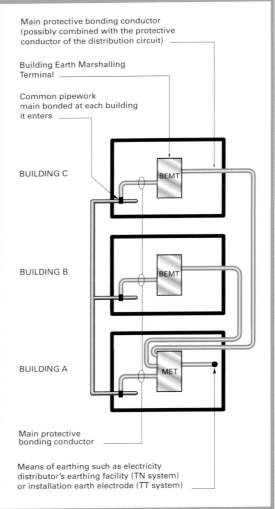

Main protective bonding conductor (possibly combined with the protective conductor of the distribution circuit)

Building Earth Marshalling Terminal

Common pipework main bonded at each building it enters

BUILDING C

BEMT

BUILDING B

BEMT

BUILDING A

MET

Main protective bonding conductor

Means of earthing such as electricity distributor's earthing facility (TN system) or installation earth electrode (TT system)

Solution

Extraneous-conductive-parts in the area served by each installation are to be connected to the Main Earthing Terminal (MET) of that installation by main protective bonding conductors complying with Chapter 54 (Regulation 411.3.1.2 refers). In addition, where an electrical installation serves more than one building, the above requirement is to be applied at each building.

A metallic pipework system entering a building, including pipework from another building, will generally be considered an extraneous-conductive-part. This is because it is liable to introduce a potential, either Earth potential or earth fault potential (from another building). As an extraneous-conductive-part, such pipework, must be main bonded.

The requirement to main bond the common metallic pipework system to the MET at each building it enters applies whether the installation in the building has its own supply of electrical energy (ie has its own separate means of earthing) or is fed from a common point of supply that serves other buildings within the complex.

In the diagram, there is only one MET (this being located at Building A), the terminal being connected by the earthing conductor to the means of earthing.

A Building Earth Marshalling Terminal (BEMT) is provided at each of Buildings B and C, these being connected to the MET by main bonding conductors. The common pipework entering Building A is main bonded directly to the MET. The common pipework entering Buildings B and C is main bonded to the appropriate BEMT (and hence to the MET). The main bonding conductors connecting the BEMTs to the MET may be formed by the circuit protective conductors of the distribution circuits supplying Buildings B and C. In this case, the cross-sectional area (csa) of the dual-function conductors must meet the requirements for each function.

Regulation 411.3.1.2 (part of)

In each installation main protective bonding conductors complying with Chapter 54 shall connect to the protective earthing terminal extraneous-conductive-parts Including the following...

Where an installation serves more than one building the above requirements shall be applied to each building.

Bonding of metal pipework

Some types of metal pipework systems have joints that do not necessarily provide good electrical continuity

Snag 48

Certain types of pipe fittings used to make joints in metal pipework systems employ seals such as O-rings and/or elastomers that cannot always be relied upon to provide electrical continuity between joined sections of pipe.

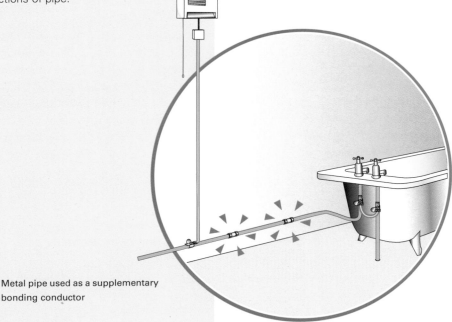

Metal pipe used as a supplementary bonding conductor

Solution

It is necessary to distinguish between pipework which is selected for use as a protective conductor (as is permitted under certain conditions by indent (vii) of Regulation 543.2.2), and pipework which is not. Having established which pipework is to be used as a protective conductor and which is not, the basic principles for determining whether compensatory measures are required to ensure electrical continuity between joined sections of pipe are as follows:

Where metal pipework incorporating joints which do not provide reliable electrical continuity is selected for use as a protective conductor, compensatory measures are required to ensure electrical continuity between the joined sections of pipe.

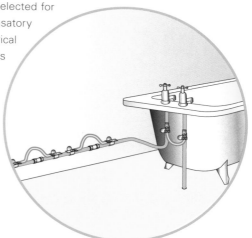

Where such metal pipework is not selected for use as a protective conductor, compensatory measures to ensure electrical continuity between the sections of pipe so joined are not required.

Regulation 543.2.2 (part of)

A protective conductor may consist of one or more of the following:

(vii) an extraneous-conductive-part complying with Regulation 543.2.6.

Extraneous-conductive-parts

Extraneous-conductive-parts are referred to extensively in *BS 7671*, mostly in relation to both main and supplementary bonding, but also with regard to electric shock protection measures such as SELV, placing out of reach and non-conducting location.

Snag 49

Do items such as radiators, metal window frames, ventilation ducts, the framework for suspended ceilings, metal baths etc require main or supplementary bonding or both, or not?

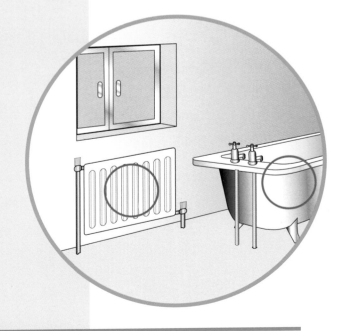

Earthing and Bonding

Solution

Most often, radiators, metal window frames, ventilation ducts, the framework for suspended ceilings and metal baths will not be extraneous-conductive-parts as defined, and where this is the case will not need protective or supplementary bonding.

The requirements of *BS 7671* concerning extraneous-conductive-parts include:

- Extraneous-conductive-parts must be connected to the Main Earthing Terminal (MET) in an installation by main protective bonding conductors where protection against electric shock is provided by Automatic Disconnection of Supply (Regulation 411.3.1.2).

- Extraneous-conductive-parts of a location containing a bath or shower may need to be connected by local supplementary equipotential bonding to the protective conductor of each circuit. (Regulation 701.415.2 refers).

The definition of an extraneous-conductive-part is: *A conductive part liable to introduce a potential, generally earth potential, and not forming part of the electrical installation.*

To decide whether a part meets the definition of an extraneous-conductive-part, the three portions of the definition must be considered:

- First portion: 'A conductive part'
- Second portion: 'liable to introduce a potential, generally earth potential'
- Third portion: 'and not forming part of the electrical installation'.

In order to decide whether or not a specific item is an extraneous-conductive-part, the following should be considered:

Is the item conductive? In order to be conductive, an item must be formed of metal or some other conducting material.

Is the item liable to introduce a potential, generally earth potential? That is to say, is the item liable to introduce a potential to a person (or livestock) who may be in contact with another potential? To introduce a potential to such a person, the item must not only be at a potential, but must also be able to introduce the potential. Introduction of the potential requires two things. The first is that the item (or a conducting item in electrical contact with it) must be accessible to be touched by a part of such a person's body. The second is that any electrical resistance through which the item is connected to the source of its potential (such as the resistance connecting an item with Earth potential) must not be so great as to prevent the potential being introduced to a person (due to voltage drop in the resistance).

Is the item part of the electrical installation? Only an item which does not form part of the electrical installation concerned may be an extraneous-conductive-part. However, items serving a non-electrical purpose within the installation should not be ruled out. Moreover, items forming part of another installation are not precluded.

Structural steel as a means of earthing

Structural steelwork can, under appropriate conditions, constitute an excellent means of earthing.

Snag 50

Designers and installers may not realise that, in many cases, the structural steelwork of a building can be used as an excellent means of earthing an installation forming part of a TT system.

Solution

Underground structural metalwork embedded in foundations, and welded metal reinforcement of concrete (except pre-stressed concrete) embedded in the Earth may be used as an installation earth electrode for an electrical installation forming part of a TT or an IT system. Such metalwork may also be used for connecting to Earth a source of supply such as the winding of a generating set.

For a particular project, it may be feasible to use such metalwork as a means of earthing. In order to make a decision upon such use, or to carry out the associated design, it will be necessary to consult the detailed guidance given in *BS 7430* and the requirements of *BS 7671*. The structural engineer must also be consulted at an early stage, and express agreement obtained that the metalwork may be used for the purpose of earthing, particularly where it is to be modified by drilling, welding or the like.

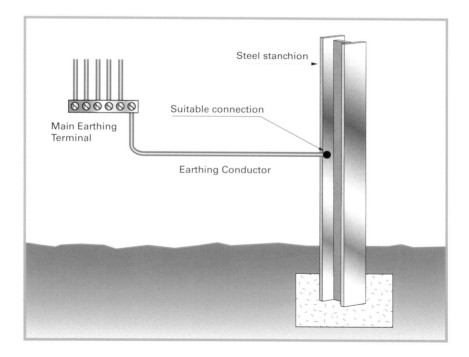

Steel stanchion

Suitable connection

Main Earthing Terminal

Earthing Conductor

Foundation metalwork in concrete can provide a ready-made and effective earth electrode, and the total electrode area formed by the underground metalwork of large structures can provide an overall value of resistance to Earth of well below 1 ohm (Clause 12.2 of *BS 7430: 1998* refers). However, careful consideration should be given to the suitability of using foundation metalwork as an earth electrode under conditions where continuous currents would flow, as corrosion of the metalwork and cracking of the surrounding concrete may result. Where significant continuous d.c. protective conductor current or current containing a d.c. component would flow, *BS 7430* recommends a main electrode, of the types described in clause 9 (plate, rod or strip) be provided to which the foundation electrodes can be bonded to provide auxiliary electrodes, this giving assistance with high fault currents.

It is important to ensure electrical continuity between all metalwork considered to be part of the earth electrode. In the case of contact between metalwork within concrete or below ground, such as reinforcing bars, electrical connection is best effected by welding. Above ground and at anchor bolts, satisfactory electrical connection is best achieved by attaching a bonding conductor to bypass each structural joint. This particularly applies to surfaces which may have been primed before assembly.

Information on methods of calculation and measurement to determine the resistance to Earth of a foundation arrangement or number of such arrangements electrically connected together is given in *BS 7430*; for example, there is likely to be an increase in this resistance over the course of time following construction.

Underground metalwork embedded in foundations includes, for example, steel stanchions encased in concrete. Above-ground structural metalwork that is electrically connected to that embedded in the foundations may be considered for use as part of the earthing conductor provided that it meets the requirements of Regulation 543.2.6 of *BS 7671* for reliability of electrical continuity and adequacy of cross-sectional area. It may be necessary to interconnect a number of foundation arrangements, possibly by use or partial use of a common structural metal frame (such as that of a building) which links them together, in order to obtain a sufficiently low resistance to Earth.

The welded metal reinforcing of concrete may be considered for use as an earth electrode but its use for such a purpose may have a detrimental effect on the structure and must have the prior agreement of the structural engineer in charge. For example, the heating of the steel reinforcing of pre-stressed concrete due to earth currents may affect the tensile strength of the structure. Where welded metal reinforcing of concrete is to be used as an earth electrode, for example the metal reinforcing in the footing of a concrete column of a building, a suitable means of connection to the welded metal reinforcing is to be provided. The earthing conductor may be connected to the metal reinforcing either below ground or above ground where it continues vertically within the column. The means of connection and its location should, however, be agreed with the structural engineer in charge. Connections may have to be made to the metalwork of a number of footings in order to obtain a sufficiently low resistance to Earth.

No less than any other connection in an installation, electrical connections to structural steelwork are subject to the requirements of Sections 526 (Electrical connections) and 522 (Selection and erection in relation to external influences) of *BS 7671*. In particular, suitable precautions must be taken against corrosion, and where a connection cannot be made accessible for inspection it must made by one of the means listed in Regulation 526.3, such as welding, soldering or brazing.

The earthing conductor connecting to the structural metalwork must be sufficiently robust and/or otherwise protected against mechanical damage and corrosion.

It must be possible to disconnect the earthing conductor from the electrode(s) for testing purposes.

Regulation 543.2.6

Except as prohibited in Regulation 543.2.1, an extraneous-conductive-part may be used as a protective conductor if it satisfies all the following requirements:

(i)   Electrical continuity shall be assured, either by construction or by suitable connection, in such a way as to be protected against mechanical, chemical or electrochemical deterioration

(ii)   The cross-sectional area shall be at least equal to that resulting from the application of Regulation 543.1.1

(iii) Unless compensatory measures are provided, precautions shall be taken against its removal

(iv) It has been considered for such use and, if necessary, suitably adapted.

Supplementary bonding in a new bathroom

A new bathroom installation rarely requires supplementary bonding.

Snag 51

A new installation in a location containing a bath or shower whether a rewire or new build, will rarely require supplementary bonding.

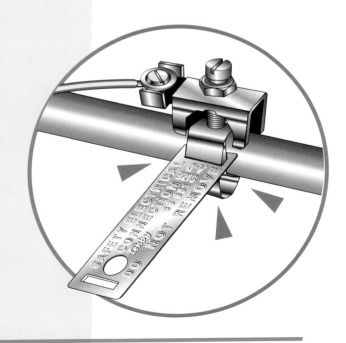

Solution

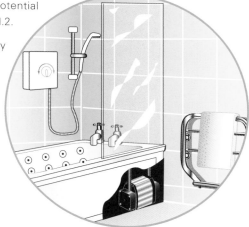

In a room containing a bath or shower, additional protection must be provided for all circuits of the location by means of an RCD having the characteristics specified in Regulation 415.1.1. (Regulation 701.411.3.3 refers). It is also required by *BS 7671* that the circuit(s) comply with the relevant requirements for automatic disconnection, such that the disconnection times will meet the requirements of Regulation Group 411.3.2, and that extraneous-conductive-parts are connected to the protective equipotential bonding according to Regulation 411.3.1.2.

In such circumstances supplementary bonding may be omitted, as indicated by Regulation 701.415.2.

Regulation 701.415.2 (part of)

Where the location containing a bath or shower is in a building with a protective equipotential bonding system in accordance with Regulation 411.3.1.2, supplementary equipotential bonding may be omitted where all of the following conditions are met:

(i) All final circuits of the location comply with the requirements for automatic disconnection according to 411.3.2

(ii) All final circuits of the location have additional protection by means of an RCD in accordance with 701.411.3.3

(iii) All extraneous-conductive-parts of the location are effectively connected to the protective equipotential bonding according to 411.3.1.2.

New circuit in an existing bathroom

Adding a new circuit in an existing installation in a location containing a bath or shower may require supplementary bonding to be installed.

Snag 52

Where a new circuit is installed for a room such as a bathroom, then additional protection must be provided for the circuit by means of an RCD having the characteristics specified in Regulation 415.1.1. (Regulation 701.411.3.3 refers).

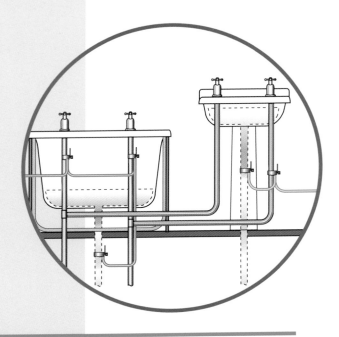

Solution

In addition, where there are other circuits serving the location then the installer will have to determine whether or not those circuits are provided with additional protection by an RCD having the characteristics specified in Regulation 415.1.1, and whether the other two conditions of Regulation 701.415.2 are met, relating to whether supplementary bonding may be omitted. If one or more of the three conditions is not met then the installer will either be required to install supplementary bonding meeting with the requirements of Regulation 701.415.2, or provide additional protection by an RCD having the characteristics of Regulation 415.1.1 for each of the existing circuits and ensure that the remaining two conditions of Regulation 701.415.2 for the omission of supplementary bonding are met.

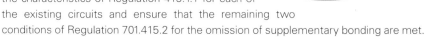

Where supplementary bonding does exist, and one or more of the three conditions required by Regulation 701.415.2 are not met, then the new circuit will need to be integrated into the existing supplementary equipotential bonding by means of a supplementary bonding conductor. This is additional to the requirement for protecting the new circuit by means of an RCD, as required by Regulation 701.411.3 and explained above.

Regulation 701.415.2 (part of)

Where the location containing a bath or shower is in a building with a protective equipotential bonding system in accordance with Regulation 411.3.1.2, supplementary equipotential bonding may be omitted where all of the following conditions are met:

(i) All final circuits of the location comply with the requirements for automatic disconnection according to 411.3.2

(ii) All final circuits of the location have additional protection by means of an RCD in accordance with 701.411.3.3

(iii) All extraneous-conductive-parts of the location are effectively connected to the protective equipotential bonding according to 411.3.1.2.

Altering existing circuits in bathrooms

Altering an existing circuit in a room containing a bath or shower may require supplementary bonding to be installed.

Snag 53

Where an existing circuit is altered, the requirements of *BS 7671* are similar to those covered in Snag 52, relating to installing a new circuit in an existing installation in a room containing a bath or shower..

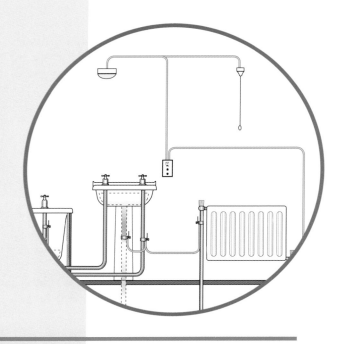

Solution

Additional protection must be provided for the altered circuit by means of an RCD having the characteristics specified in Regulation 415.1.1. (Regulation 701.411.3.3 refers).

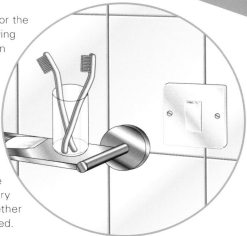

In addition, where there are other circuits serving the location the installer will have to determine whether, or not, those circuits have additional protection by an RCD having the characteristics of Regulation 415.1.1 and whether the other two requirements of Regulation 701.415.2 are met relating to whether supplementary bonding may be omitted, or whether supplementary bonding is already installed.

Where supplementary bonding **does not** exist then the installer will either be required to install supplementary bonding in line with the requirements of Regulation 701.415.2, or provide additional protection by an RCD having the characteristics specified in Regulation 415.1.1 for each of the existing circuits and ensure that the remaining two requirements of Regulation 701.415.2 for the omission of supplementary bonding are met.

Where supplementary bonding **does** exist then the altered circuit will require either to be integrated into the existing supplementary equipotential bonding by means of a supplementary bonding conductor, or meet all three requirements of Regulation 701.415.2 for the omission of supplementary bonding. This is additional to the requirement for protecting the altered circuit by means of an RCD, as required by Regulation 701.411.3 and explained above.

Regulation 415.1.1

The use of RCDs with a rated residual operating current ($I_{\Delta n}$) not exceeding 30 mA and an operating time not exceeding 40 ms at a residual current of 5 $I_{\Delta n}$, is recognized in a.c. systems as additional protection in the event of failure of the provision for basic protection and/or the provision for fault protection or carelessness by users.

Regulation 701.411.3.3

Additional protection shall be provided for all circuits of the location, by the use of one or more RCDs having the characteristics specified in Regulation 415.1.1.

---

snags and solutions part 1   Published by NICEIC. © Electrical Safety Council (JAN 2008) (3rd Ed.)

Index by subject